Michael Bl

The Risk Business

Industry and the Designers

THE
DESIGN
COUNCIL

The Risk Business

First edition published in the United Kingdom
1979 by Design Council
28 Haymarket, London SW1Y 4SU

Designed by Anne Fisher

Printed and bound in the United Kingdom by
Hazell Watson & Viney Ltd
Aylesbury, Bucks

Distributed by
Heinemann Educational Books Ltd
22 Bedford Square, London WC1B 3HH

British Library CIP Data
Blakstad, Michael
    The Risk Business.
    1. Technological innovations
    2. Design, Industrial – Management
    I. Title
    658.5' 7   HD45
ISBN 0 85072 098 2

Contents

This book is dedicated to Karen, Anna-Sofie and Matthew, and above all to Tricia, because it represents a great deal of time that would otherwise have been spent with them.

About Designers

Many of those whose work is described in this book would not think of themselves as designers. Engineers, perhaps, or chief executives, project leaders, inventors, entrepreneurs or scientists; but many of them have never stood at a drawing board and most have never been inside an art or design college in their lives.

Some, on the other hand, such as the very creative teams at Ogle and Pentagram, are career designers in the strictest sense of the words and might be surprised to find themselves between the same covers as the mixed bag I have listed above. There are, of course, reasons for spreading the net so widely in attempting to describe the work of designers in industry. In the first place, the world of manufacturing does in truth offer a greater diversity of roles to the designer than any other field. A 'new design' of product, of production line, of corporate image, of working method, of working environment . . . the phrase fits equally well into all these contexts and more. It is particularly encouraging to see how the term 'designer' is often used to describe an engineer who is working in his most innovatory, most stimulating capacity.

Because I have cast the design net so wide, I hope that this book will serve as a route map for those attempting to find their way through the bewildering and sometimes faceless world in which most men and women are destined to spend the bulk of their waking hours, and upon whose success and ability to create wealth for the nation the rest of us certainly depend for our livelihood. I have enormously enjoyed the contacts with the manufacturers of Britain and America provided by my work, and I hope that this book will help others to share that pleasure.

But there is another, sneakier reason for my choice of 'suitable cases for treatment'. The bewildering and faceless world of industry is an obstinate, amoeboid target for the television producer or the writer to tackle. So often it seems that the important events and individuals are invisible, if not non-existent, phenomena, and that decisions are taken by dint of committees, memoranda, pecking orders and – ultimately – by default. The outsider in search of a clear-cut story to tell finds himself desperately peeling away the onion skins of management hierarchies and specialist departments until he finds himself with nothing and nobody at the core.

The designer seems to me to stem this tide of anonymity triumphantly. However much industrial designers may proclaim that their work is hemmed in by unsympathetic finance directors, short-sighted marketing men and incompetent production managers, the fact is that they, uniquely, are afforded the privilege of creating a product, of building their bread-board model or prototype, of saying at the end of the day 'a small thing but (largely) mine own'. They also stand at the fascinating point at which the paths cross between the various disciplines that go to form today's complex industrial organisation. However much the designer's creativity may seem to be obstructed by others, the fact remains that the research and development men, the market surveyors, the accountants, the works supervisors, the quality controllers and the rest do come to the designer – and he to them – and this interplay does give him an extraordinarily broad view of industry at work. He has to be as conscious of the potential market for his product as the sales team, as familiar with the technicalities of production as the toolsetter, and as sensitive to the cost and potential profit as that all-important figure the finance director.

Because the designer occupies this unique position, and because he is an individual with an identifiable role, he and his artefacts have tended more than any others to find their way in front of the harsh lights which we, the television people, carry round in our search for subjects that combine both the human and the mechanical interest that are necessary to bring industry to life on the television screen. The BBC Television programme 'The Risk Business' which stimulated me to write this book (although I should make it clear that it is not 'the book of the programme', simply an extension of my personal experiences) has grown out of the long-running 'Tomorrow's World' series, which has a unique reputation for reporting the positive achievements of scientists and technologists in Britain and abroad. This book reflects the work of a team of a dozen or so people – producers, researchers and myself – who have been attempting to build on the solid 'Tomorrow's World' foundation a more detailed and more human account of the positive achievements of these same pioneers, and particularly of those working in manufacturing industry. By no means all the stories have happy endings, but in none of them was the work done by the protagonists less than admirable, and occasionally it was heroic. My thanks are, without doubt, due to the unstinted efforts of those with whom I work at the BBC; they are also due to the very courageous designers and other entrepreneurs who were willing to open up to us the most sensitive nerve endings of their working lives.

Michael Blakstad

Chapter One

Truck

One of the most ambitious design ventures of the 1970s,
providing a unique glimpse into the carefully laid strategy
behind a new range of trucks planned to take Leyland Vehicles
profitably into the next century

The most casual visitor to Leyland Vehicles during 1977 could
hardly have failed to catch sight of one or more giant, lumbering,
almost grotesque trucks jolting down the cobbled test track or
simply moving from one part of the site to another. Had he got
closer to these monsters, he would have been intrigued to observe
that their unlikely appearance was the result of elaborate false
panels and disguised window frames. These were fastened onto

Heavily disguised, a prototype truck takes to the test track

the prototypes for the company's biggest design and manufacturing project of all time, a new range of heavy trucks, planned to carry Leyland into the next century with a set of products that would enable the company to revive their previously honourable division as one of BL's few profit-making areas.

The motor industry has always worried deeply about publicity leaks. Ostensibly, this is for fear of letting rivals catch sight of the result of years of careful design and test work, although in fact there must surely be a limit to the number of changes another manufacturer will make to his own development programme, which may be the outcome of as much as 10 years of work, as the result of a telephoto glimpse of his competitor's new baby. A more realistic fear must be the loss of sales of an existing range of cars or trucks should the press publish photos of an exciting new model with the news that it is about to be launched. Up to early 1978 Leyland's truck sales were slipping; from a market share of 23·3 per cent in 1976, the overall annual figure for 1977 was less than 20 per cent, with some months as low as 17·2 per cent, and that was in a buoyant market. Their heavyweight contender, the Marathon, was openly admitted not to have a lengthy future; it had been a stop-gap compromise designed around available parts and assembly equipment, and the trucking industry had known for years that the end of the decade would give birth to a new range of Leyland trucks.

It was brave of Leyland to let 'The Risk Business' visit their Truck and Bus division (as it then was) more than two years before their new model was due to be released to the public. Our cameras were only allowed to show the design mock-ups hidden beneath heavy shrouds, but we were given access to a great deal of the information and philosophy behind the development work, which was a noble act by a set of people who have consistently received a bad press and who had a great deal to lose. Long the most profitable part of the Leyland conglomerate, Truck and Bus had seen their earnings continually ploughed back into the national save-the-car campaign with the result that their vehicles had been consistently under-financed. It was not until Lord Ryder decided in 1975 to allocate £350 million of the £2·8 billion government grant towards financing the new trucks that the division was able to think seriously about a major new investment and to take the mental wraps off their long-nurtured plans.

These plans were centred on a whole range of trucks, all designed and assembled in a coherent, modular style. It was the so-called Advanced Design Group, led by Keith Hemmings, that had turned its collective mind to replacing the Marathon and eventually, in the fullness of time, Leyland's other vehicles, with something other than a succession of one-off designs. In 1972 they had spent fully six months preparing one of the largest feasibility studies ever undertaken in the British motor industry. It had 42 different headings, ranging from the most technical tooling requirements to the most far-reaching marketing plans. They established, for instance, that Leyland would do well to concentrate first on producing the heavy truck, not only because this represented the prestige end of the range, but also for the bald commercial reason that there is more profit per sale on a heavy truck than a light one. They proposed that the new trucks should show what they termed 'low aggressivity'; back in the early 1970s there was a strong and growing popular antagonism to juggernauts, so the group believed that cabs should be designed to look less dominant, radiator grilles more unobtrusive, and the whole profile 'low'. Energy, they reckoned, would be at a premium by the 1980s, so everything possible should be done to save fuel through the use of styling and weight-saving materials. Noise should be reduced, partly to cause less inconvenience to the public, partly to improve the lot of the driver who was now making himself felt as a vital influence in deciding which truck his employer should buy. It was also for the sake of the driver that the group wanted attention paid to cooling systems. In the current models, large primitive ducts created an ugly hump in the floor of the cab which made it harder for the occupant to move freely about the interior. The cab, after all, is not only workplace but also hotel room for the long-distance trucker.

And so the 42 articles went on – we shall be coming back to them time and again as we meet the designers of the new trucks – but by far the most important conclusion reached by Hemmings and the team was the radical proposal that the whole design concept should be modular; that the same tooling, the same basic parts that were now to be designed for the 44-ton premium lorries, should be capable of being used for trucks of different sizes, if and when Leyland decided that other trucks in their range needed to be replaced. The designers of the 'truck for the 1980s' should, in effect, also be designing trucks of different sizes for the 1990s and even into the next century.

The key to this concept was the most visible and most expensive part of the truck, the section that requires the most tooling and into which the largest number of different features has to be built – the driver's cab. The 42 articles specified that the same basic cab design should suffice for the whole future range of trucks. The cab itself would have to match all vehicle operating requirements as well as different engine fitments, chassis designs and wheel diameters. In effect, between 1978 and the end of the century all Leyland trucks were to be assembled from a Meccano kit of basic parts.

Some of Leyland's aggressive-looking competitors

When the Truck and Bus Division received the go-ahead, after Ryder's 1975 hand-out, they were faced immediately with an important decision as to the design team best equipped to handle the mammoth project. They could have gone to Italy's Michelotti group, with whom they had had dealings in the past. Leyland's own Austin Morris Car Group designers were itching for a chance to extend their expertise. The private Lionel Sherrow agency had just completed a successful contract with Scania on their new range. Ogle Design had been acquiring a lot of relevant experience through their liaison with the important cab builders, Motor Panels. There was a certain amount of national pride at stake, should the contract go overseas. There was a degree of internal Leyland sensitivity, should the car division be overlooked. In the end, a competition was held (though Michelotti were not invited to enter). It was taken very seriously indeed – one agency sent as many as 300 drawings to be considered, and had to send a designer up to Leyland to go through them with Hemmings for fear the judges would be overwhelmed – and the contract was decided by the Leyland Board.

The contract was duly awarded to the Ogle team, headed by Tom Karen who had taken over as managing director following the death of the firm's founder, David Ogle. For Karen and the Ogle team this was by no means a flash in an entirely new pan. Since the beginning of the decade they had been working with Motor Panels Ltd, one of the country's leading specialists in the construction of truck cabs. Ogle had designed (and BBC's 'Tomorrow's World' had demonstrated) the MPO cab which, at the time, was the nearest thing to a luxury ocean liner's cabin that any trucker could ever hope to enter. Apart from other work with Plaxton's coaches, the rest of Ogle's motor design work had been with cars (the Reliant Scimitar, the Ogle Mini and, most recently, the Lucas Taxi) but Ogle had worked long and hard on preparing for this contract, and when it came they were well prepared to undertake the largest job any agency had ever been contracted to handle. From 1973 almost all of Ogle's staff of 50 designers, draughtsmen and prototype builders were involved on this project at one time or another, and although Ogle continued with many other jobs (including some intriguing work with – of all things – toys) there is no doubt that the T45, as the new truck was to be called, became a seven-day-a-week obsession during the next five years for Karen and his team.

It is now time to meet the man whose job it was, during the vital first three years of the T45 project, to hold the whole enterprise together. Dealing with a firm of consultant designers based in Letchworth, a group of in-house designers up at Leyland in Lancashire, and also with production engineers (the men who were not only going to build the truck, but a £32 million new plant to handle the assembly), the man holding the strings of a project like this had to be a very big man indeed. Ron Ellis, then managing director of Truck and Bus, was a very big man. Virtually the only member of Leyland's top brass to survive the Ryder purge unscathed, Ron Ellis had worked for Leyland since joining them as an apprentice back in 1941. He took an external degree in engineering at Manchester University, then rose rapidly through the layers of management to his top job at Truck and Bus and a position on the Board.

Ellis's style of management was intensely personal, exercising his own brand of involving and motivating those around him. It seemed that his every waking hour was spent communicating with his team; even when driving to and from work he used a cassette machine and a microphone slung round his neck in order to listen to, and reply to, enquiries or complaints from his designers and engineers. He met Keith Hemmings every fortnight to discuss progress on the T45, and every six weeks held a larger, but still informal, meeting with all the teams involved in the new project. His philosophy spread right through his division: one of the most convincing sequences in the programme we made about the project featured a discussion held by John Briffitt, plant director and Harold Musgrove, director of operations, at 7.30 one morning with two of the design engineers, Jim Mason and Bob Beresford. The issue was whether a cross-member should be fitted to the chassis before or after the engine had been put in position – an awkward job in itself because the member had to be bolted at a difficult angle. Perhaps because of the early hour, but perhaps because even a seemingly mundane matter can arouse considerable emotion when all concerned are passionate about their work, the four protagonists completely forgot about the presence of the camera; Briffitt in particular was adamant that the cross-member was badly designed. 'It could be as much as half a hole out', he proclaimed, while Mason was convinced that the answer lay in widening the frame slightly. Briffitt wasn't letting him off: 'I'm talking about assembling it, not fitting it; nobody's going to be able to get their drills in . . .' and he offered to show Mason what he meant by a couple of selective assemblies. As the meeting finished, Mason bet Briffitt a pint that his design would work but as so often happens, the bet was never put to the test. Torsion tests on the gruelling pavé circuit proved that the chassis was too weak (for other reasons) at this precise point, and a much simpler redesign eliminated the difficulty.

Dialogues like this, at every possible level of the enterprise, characterised the full period spent designing and developing the T45. Thanks largely to Ellis's belief that ideas should be encouraged to pass freely up, down and across the organisation, there was a continual flow of designers, managers, engineers and production men through the closely guarded doors of the prototype shop, and the engineering and test bays of Leyland's Truck and Bus Division. There was a similar flow up and down the M1 and M6 between Letchworth and Leyland with countless meetings, black coffee, and a mountain of sandwiches consumed in conference rooms at both ends of the motorways.

Karen describes the Advanced Design Group's 42 articles as an extraordinarily tidy brief. Some of the more general aspects of the document have already been mentioned, but for the designers there was even more value in the minutiae of the specifications. Take the aerodynamics: a successful cab design that produces a smooth passage of air across the exterior of a vehicle does not just reduce drag and thus increase fuel efficiency, it also has important side-effects including – of all things – keeping the side windows clean.

The airflow specifications had a major effect on the final shape of the cab. The original Ogle design featured a crisp line around the front of the cab which emphasised the outline shape. The effect, thought the designers, would be to enable the onlooker to 'read the sides', and take note of the overall appearance of the cab. To emphasise this outline, Ogle had conceived a very slightly concave rim framing the entire pod, but when this design was tested in the wind-tunnel, the hollow caught the passing air and broke the flow, not only causing poor performance but also enabling the dirt thrown up by other vehicles to plaster the near-side window. A clean airflow would have carried this dirt away from the window and saved the driver having, from time to time, to pull up, walk round the cab, and wipe off the muck!

Another feature that affected the airflow was the position of the two pillars fore and aft of the cab (the so-called A and B posts) and the corner above the windscreen. Ogle's initial design for the roof line proved to be at a little too sharp an angle, and extensive wind-tunnel tests showed that it should be altered by

Ogle's first design for the T45 with a crisp cab outline

just one eighth of an inch. This hardly affected the overall appearance of the cab but, combined with the departure of the concave line around the whole pod, the changes led the Ogle thinking into a whole new phase. At this point, having abandoned the idea of a crisp outline, Tom Karen started to think again about the overall aspect of the cab he was designing.

Most trucks are designed to draw the passer-by's attention straight to the radiator grille, presumably because the grille happens to be at the same height above the road as the motorist in a car. It is on the grille that the brand name of the manufacturer is often carried and it is certainly here that the most striking design features are clustered. Karen surmised that in fact the attention of the other road users was more likely to be drawn to the windscreen of a truck, because that was where the driver sat, and human beings generally prefer to look at other members of their species. Windscreens are dark, and Ogle decided to carry that thought further by introducing a bold black panel, or 'pouch', directly under the windscreen, to extend the dark area and create a coherent top half to the whole design. It was on this pouch that the Leyland name would be carried in large white lettering, and in fact the panel served more than a cosmetic purpose in that it was hinged to allow access to the windscreen washer bottles. But Karen stresses that the main intention in introducing the black pouch was aesthetic. 'What pleased me', he says, 'was to give the cab a distinct character. When you saw it half a mile away you knew that you were looking at a Leyland truck.'

The 42 articles had, it seems, played an important if indirect part in deciding the format of the cab. Without the stress they had placed on aerodynamic performance that concave rim would perhaps have lasted much longer in the design concept and, who knows, Karen's mind might never have started working on the idea of drawing attention away from the sides of the cab and towards the upper half of the pod. But there was one field in which the specifications of the engineers and the aspirations of the designers came into direct conflict – the interior of the cab and the layout of the instrument panel.

When Ogle started on the contract, they were given a wooden mock-up of the layout of the driver's controls and were asked, more or less, to work round it. This was by no means an arbitrary action; Leyland in fact employed a human factors engineer, Barry Brooks, whose team had put months of pioneering research work into finding the precise positions in which the various controls would be most ergonomically efficient for the driver and which would also, with economy always in mind, involve as few changes as possible when the layout had to be reversed for overseas sales and left-hand-drive vehicles. The engineer's jargon for compo-

The second Ogle design embodied the distinctive dark windscreen pouch

nents that have to be produced separately for Britain and the rest of the world is 'handed' parts; Leyland wanted the mirror-image of their controls to involve as few 'handed' components as possible. This meant in effect that there should be three units: the driver's instrument panel, which of course moved with the driver; a central unit containing the ventilation controls, which was completely flat and would be identical for both 'hands'; and the passenger's panel, which was a pretty simple affair and again travelled across the cab for overseas models.

There was no attempt whatsoever at styling in the wooden mock-up prepared by the ergonomics team, but it was so detailed that there appeared to be very little opportunity left for the Ogle team to originate a styling concept. Their initial horror was, admittedly, turned to something closer to sympathy for the work Leyland had done once the designers had undergone a rigorous two-day briefing as to the exact reason for every single decision taken by Brooks and his team. Nothing, it seemed, had been forgotten; the thickness of the steering wheel, the load the driver could bring to bear on the clutch, the distance at which every control could comfortably be located from the driver, right down to the precise angle of the accelerator in the truck's cruising state. Ogle were anxious to change the somewhat cumbersome shape of the gear lever by the driver's left hand, but the stick in a 44-ton

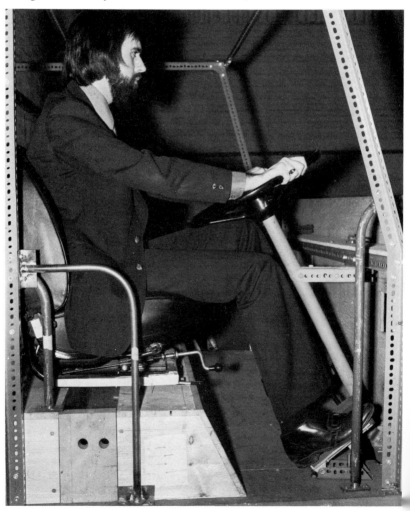

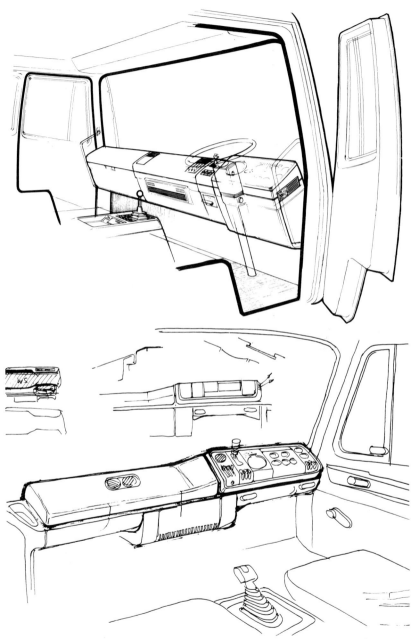

Opposite: Barry Brooks, Leyland's ergonomist, at the mock-up cab controls
The team's initial cab layout (top) with a minimum of 'handed' elements, and (bottom)
Tom Karen's sketch redesign

truck is no mere gear-shift; it contains the control for the 'splitter', which effectively doubles the number of gear ratios available, and Karen's attempts to style this elaborate column were, he now admits, largely futile. He did manage to hide the 10 centimetres or so of bare metal that showed between the gate and the handle, but that was all. However, this was less significant than what Karen saw as the over-complicated layout of the proposed instrument panel and controls. Both he and Leyland desperately wanted to tidy up the cluster of controls around the driver, and in particular he wanted to shape the central ventilator unit so that it rose gently towards the driver's unit and thus broke the harsh, monotonous line of the ergonomic mock-up. Inevitably, if it rose in one direction towards a right-hand driver, it would have to rise in the opposite direction towards his Continental equivalent, so Karen was running counter to the original requirement for a minimum of handed units. This, however, was one battle that he did succeed in winning, and it enabled him also to improve the layout of the ventilator controls. With a certain amount of attention to detail he was able to improve the looks of the dashboard and also the roof-mounted instrument panel above the windscreen. The final interior was the result of months of hard to-and-fro negotiations between designers and engineers, but it was a very handsome creation. It compared favourably with the standards of many an expensive limousine, and sitting in the driver's seat you felt not unlike the skipper of a jumbo jet, with instruments clustered conveniently to both hand and eye.

Another battle-front, and one on which the designers lost comprehensively, concerned the interior colour scheme. Ogle wanted a bold livery, and Tom Karen still looks a little sad as he shows pictures of the fiery red he had for some months hoped would be offered as an optional scheme – crisp, clean, and instantly identifiable. Alas, the colour was so bold that it would surely have clashed with some if not most of the hues in which customers would have wanted to paint the exterior of their trucks, and furthermore the red would be a difficult colour to match inside. If the firms that supplied ready-made plastics or vinyl components for the cab were to miss the exact colour specified by Leyland, even slightly, the effect would be an unpleasant clash of violent tones. In the final design the seats are a gentle plaid of grey, blue and a little red, while the carpet and panels are an inoffensive grey.

The human factors team featured once more in a good example of positive co-operation between Ogle and the Leyland engineers – the grab handle and the steps that help the driver to steady himself when getting into and out of the cab. In the past such handles had been simple, small affairs that were of limited value

The T45 cab interior in its final, production form

to the driver because they were either too far away from him while he was on the ground, causing him to stretch an uncomfortable and unhelpful distance, or they were too close to his chest when his feet were on the floor of the cab. The T45's grab handle was almost a metre long, with a hint of a bend in it to break its visual impact. The steps themselves were angled away from the cab, which made it possible for the driver to see where he was

21

putting his feet (incredible that this was actually an innovation in the truck business!) and above all, the steps featured the sausage.

The sausage, believe it or not, was the key symbol for the new range of trucks. It all started when the designers were drawing up the door handle and the recess in the nearby panel that would enable the driver to slide his fingers under the rim of the door to

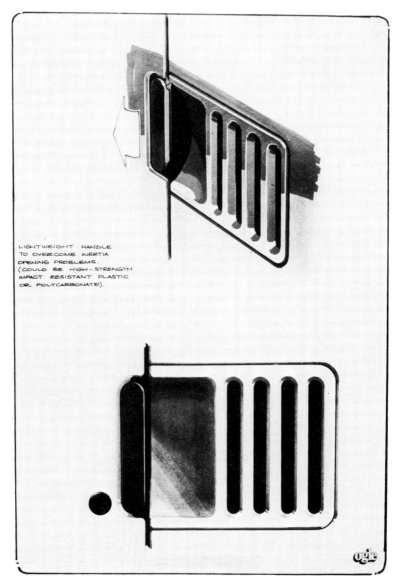

LIGHTWEIGHT HANDLE
TO OVERCOME INERTIA
OPENING PROBLEMS.
(COULD BE HIGH-STRENGTH
IMPACT RESISTANT PLASTIC
OR POLYCARBONATE).

open it. To Karen, the moment at which a driver first touched the truck was of supreme importance: it was the psychological point at which he made direct contact with the hunk of metal he was going to drive and perhaps buy. The first design left a sausage-shaped recess for the hand to reach the door release button. Karen's eye returned time and again to the button; soon he had redesigned the handle so that the recess itself was part of a larger unit with four sausages – they gave ventilation – livening up the otherwise stark feature. Ogle then found that they could put sausage shapes – slightly curved this time – into the surface of the gear clutch and brake pedals so they helped the foot to grip. They tried a sausage-shaped grip for the gear lever but, as we have seen, the design could not be reconciled with the complicated controls the lever had to house. But, most importantly, the sausages began to appear on the outside of the cab, both front and back, and above all to play their part in the radiator grille . . . but more of that later.

Designing the cab for a new range of trucks is in many ways the epitome of industrial design in that it illustrates to perfection the constant to-ing and fro-ing between, on the one hand, the designer, with his desire for crisp style and distinctive appearance, and on the other, the engineers, who know what is technically possible, and who are constantly aware of the accountants and marketing people and their insistence on strict cost control and

Early drawings of the door handle (opposite) and the production version – the birth of the sausage motif

a price that customers can afford. Yet another example of this dialogue comes from the windows at the side of the cab.

The Ogle team had, as we have seen, moved the emphasis at the front of the cab away from the outline and towards the windscreen and the pouch beneath it, and in doing so they had met their mandate, in the 42 articles, to 'reduce aggressivity'. They had compounded this trend by rounding off the corners at the front of the cab, so that the pod only filled out to its full width some distance from the front; this receding effect not only improved the airflow, but it also made the truck appear slightly slimmer than it in fact was. The Ogle team wanted to continue this effect with side windows that tapered upwards from the front since this would in turn not only improve the aspect of the cab, but also give the driver a better view of the kerb below his feet. No one in engineering disputed the desirability of both of these factors; it was simply a question of cost. The greater the expanse of glass, the higher the cost, and in the end the two teams were actually haggling over the last half inch of glass. There, you could say, is the essence of truck design!

Another source of dispute was the often forgotten back of the cab. The main question here centred on whether there should be windows behind the driver's head or not, and the discussion divided into two slightly different camps. It seemed to the designers *and* the engineers that drivers were not keen on windows behind their heads; especially when carrying large and potentially insecure loads, the driver liked to feel that there was something more substantial than a sheet of glass between his head and a rod of steel that just might shift and run forwards towards the cab. The marketing people, on the other hand, liked windows; they were aware that the people who bought lorries were very often not drivers, and they liked to stress the good, light aspect of a cab with windows and the better visibility towards the rear (although in fact drivers generally reverse using mirrors or with their heads out of the side windows). In this case the marketing men won, though designers and engineers had a bet that drivers would keep the curtains drawn to keep the sun off the back of their necks! For added protection, the T45 had an extra skin of metal all over the back – except where there were windows – and the whole rear fascia was liberally littered with sausage-shaped indentations!

The long hot summer of 1976 proved to be the most intense period in what had never been an idle schedule. At both Letchworth and Leyland meetings went on through the night, designs were drawn, redrawn, and redrawn yet again. Deadlines were set by the engineers, anxious to complete plans for their enormous new assembly plant, and then broken to make way for another set of dates. To cap it all, a major change of personnel was about to take place at Leyland.

Ron Ellis's position in the early development of the T45 has already been described; it was his baby and everyone on the project was well aware that he was working for Ellis. It was Ellis

The back of the T45 cab – with windows

who gave the go-ahead to the final design, and the manner in which he took the decision was indicative of how tight the schedule was. He couldn't be in Lancashire on the day on which the final mock-up was completed, but the design team took a series of Polaroid photographs and had them driven to Ellis in London. He knew the truck well enough not to need any additional information. He gave the nod, and it was all systems go for the Motor Show in October 1978 (the first time that cars and commercial vehicles would be displayed together).

It must have been at very much the same time that summer that Ron Ellis took Patrick Uden, the producer of this edition of 'The Risk Business', and myself to one side in the new Berkeley Hotel in London and told us what no one in Leyland, apart from Alex Park and Lord Ryder, knew – that he, Ellis, was about to be seconded from British Leyland to become Britain's Head of Defence Sales at the Ministry of Defence. For us at the time it was a disturbing piece of information, because we had completed filming but there was still a fortnight to go before transmission and Ron Ellis couldn't guarantee that the news would not leak out before that date. In fact, it didn't, but the impact on our programme would in any case have been insignificant beside the

The T45 as it was left by Ron Ellis . . .

possible effect of Ellis's departure on the Truck and Bus Division in general, and on the T45 in particular.

It was not long before Ellis's replacement was named: Des Pitcher, not a mechanical engineer like his predecessor, but a graduate of the electronics industry. Pitcher's first visit to the prototype shop, where he would see the approved model of the T45, was awaited with some trepidation. There was a strong feeling among those working on the project that the truck was Ellis's and that Pitcher had no right to interfere. In any case, changes to the design at that stage could only be very expensive, and would greatly reduce the truck's chance of making the 1978 Motor Show.

But in the event, if Ellis was the begetter of the T45, it was Pitcher who brought it to maturity. When he saw the truck, Pitcher's instructions were few in number, but they bit deeply into the design philosophy. The first change he requested was for a vertical grille, to replace the long, horizontal grille of the Ellis format, which seemed to some of those involved to be a step backwards from the 'low aggressivity' and gentle appearance for which they had striven. Tom Karen had in fact also been worried about the horizontal grille, because the strips were long and thin and might well have proved too weak to support themselves for

. . . and as subsequently modified under Des Pitcher, his successor

27

the full length and so needed ugly reinforcing bars. The other change Pitcher wanted was to have larger, bolder indicators: they gave a crisper edge to the infill panel, but this was no consolation to the production engineers who now had to rethink the construction of the front of the cab.

We left the front end of the cab at the point where the Ogle team had decided to concentrate on the panel below the windscreen and curve the corners to give a gentler face to the truck, but there was a great deal more to the design of the cab than that. For instance, one of the most difficult jobs was to make it possible for the whole cab to tilt forward to give maintenance staff access to the engine and chassis directly under the cab. Some cabs required the bonnet itself to be opened first, to make room at the front for the cab to tilt; other designs had large obtrusive lumps above the radiator, either because these contained the hinges on which the cab tilted or because the pintle (the pin to which tow bars are attached) could not be concealed behind the panel work. The T45 designers decided early on that the panel between the radiator and the pouch – the infill panel – would have to solve all these problems and a few more besides.

First, the hinges were incorporated into the infill panel itself and the pintle, welded to the chassis frame, was built behind the infill panel where it could be reached through a removable panel. The problem now was clearance: as the cab tilted forward, some room was needed between the swivelling cab and the fixed bumper, and this was to be accommodated by an 'upside-down mouth' at the bottom of the infill panel. The designers were not slow to see that this gave them an excellent opportunity to give the driver, literally, a leg-up: they put an alloy plate into this crevice on which he could stand to reach and clean his windscreen.

So far, so good, but the all-important headlights, and radiator grille had still to find their place in the design. It's no exaggeration to say that these had, in one combination or another, slid all over the pod, the infill panel and the radiator for a considerable time, making their presence felt in various ways according to a combination of design and engineering criteria that would bewilder an outsider. The headlights, for example, would look better and give better vision if they were specially designed, large and perhaps square lamps, but if they were unique to one range of trucks they would be expensive to produce and, perhaps more important, difficult to replace in remote countries. The radiator grilles, of course, were to be long horizontal sausages, though they had indeed made one or two appearances at the base of the pod in a vertical configuration. To move them meant redesigning the production machinery, and that meant delays. So it was that, in the autumn of 1976, the designers and engineers were once more on the home straight, but with that 1978 Motor Show looking ever less likely as a deadline.

Pitcher was responsible for the partial demise of 'low aggressivity', though the production model was still to be a much more friendly truck than its predecessors and most of its rivals – the sausages somehow took the edge off the tiger's snarl! How well had the rest of the 42 articles survived the various stages of development? Some of the original requirements had, it must be admitted, been deferred for later models in the range. High costs had put paid to the idea of an 'active safety' concept, though the lower part of the front of the cab had at one stage been designed in such a way that it would have given way on impact, leaving the driver of a colliding car with a much higher chance of survival. It's only possible to be noble, safety conscious and the rest, say Leyland, if it doesn't price you out of the market. No single firm can afford to take a lead in this respect; it must be up to the legislators to insist that all trucks meet the same safety code and, if such laws are ever passed, it will be simple for Leyland to brush the dust off its existing plans.

The dream of a walk-through cab without a hump in the middle also had to wait for future generations of truck; the engineers were not able to develop a small enough cooling unit and duct at the stipulated price. But in other respects the 42 articles were triumphantly met, and above all the Ogle design left the manufacturers with an extraordinary number of open options. During all the five years of development, the European Economic Community vacillated and found itself obstructed as it attempted to introduce legislation standardising axle weights and engine capacity, and in many cases it was the British who stood in the way of agreement. The design brief required that the trucks should be capable of fitting any engine size within reason, and of catering for any axle weight. The chassis could, in fact, be engineered completely separately from the cab, so modifications here were relatively easy should the EEC take an unexpected turn in its policy, and the Leyland team was, and is, confident of being able to cater for any likely specification. In the meantime the truck can be made for both the British and the European markets, different though they are, with minimal alteration to the tooling.

For the future, the gentle curves of the bodywork do not just look good, they make it possible to manufacture the cab out of lighter, but less ductile, aluminium should a fuel crisis bring weight restrictions as in America. The team is looking at the possibility that noise may have to be reduced in cities, at the chance that impact standards may be introduced, and at a host of other possible developments. After all, the cab design and the

29

chassis that supports it are going to take Leyland Vehicles into the next century, come what may. In many different ways the programme has been a triumph that deserves to be hailed and rewarded in the market-place.

But at the time of writing, a cloud of uncertainty has descended over the project. The truck is late, though how late no one quite knows. The new chairman of BL has expressed disquiet at the relatively poor performance of the Vehicles company in 1977 and 1978, and Des Pitcher resigned in July 1978 to return to the electronics industry whence he originally came. The manufacturing lines are not yet ready, and that October 1978 deadline has certainly gone by the board. But none of that should detract from the fact that Karen, Hemmings, Brooks, and a number of other designers and engineers whose names have not been mentioned, have achieved everything that was asked of them. From just one and a half sets of tooling, it will be possible to manufacture both the large premium cab for the 44 tonners and – when management takes the decision – a smaller cab for the lightweight trucks and vans as well.

The year 1979 will see a cab that fits the rugged goliaths designed for overseas markets, the tankers and other kings of the

The production T45, ready for the road in Leyland livery

road. But a slice out of the infill panel here, a smaller windscreen there, the removal of the driver's bunk and a few other minor alterations to components and to tooling, and the same basic design will produce a cab for the lightweight delivery trucks, furniture vans and other smaller vehicles with which Leyland must one day replace its other models. Behind every variation, every aspect of the design of these trucks, lie the years of agonising, testing, debating and compromising described in this chapter. Look hard at the new Leyland trucks when they're on the road; they deserve a lot of attention.

Chapter Two

Care and Concern

Crisis this time begets challenge as Clarks, an old-established
shoe company, turn to designers inside and outside the firm to
build a new corporate image and new products with which to
fight a flood of imported footwear

For a century and a half, C & J Clark Limited have thrived on
care and concern. You can almost reach out and feel the
benevolence as you enter the one-company town of Street, a
former coaching village in the heart of Somerset, which has grown
and prospered round this single shoe company. You can sense
care and concern as you walk round the spacious, well lit factory
premises in which Clarks shoes are assembled by one of the few
remaining workforces who, in these days of high technology, are
privileged to touch, smell and understand the product their craft
is producing. Finally, you can experience it for yourself if you buy
shoes at a Clarks' retail outlet and have them fitted by the only
people permitted to sell you Clarks shoes – staff who have been
on the special training courses at Street and elsewhere where they
are taught that feet, and especially growing feet, are to be cared
for and fitted with the correct shoes.

Through this care and concern, generations of British school-
chidren grew to associate the trade name Clarks with mother's
devotion, school discipline and with much that was strict and
thoughtful in their lives. It also proved to be a successful sales
formula, elevating Clarks to the status of Britain's largest private
manufacturing company, and the most successful shoe company
in Europe.

But then came the rub. First, the 'age of consent', at which
children were permitted to choose the shoes *they* liked, dropped.
At schools, shoes ceased to be as strictly regimented as they once
were, and increasingly became the medium through which youngsters could show off the latest trends. What was more, the post-
war baby boom on which the shoe industry had prospered began,
in the early 1970s, to develop into a child famine. Clarks had
relied heavily on their children's shoes: they not only sold shoes

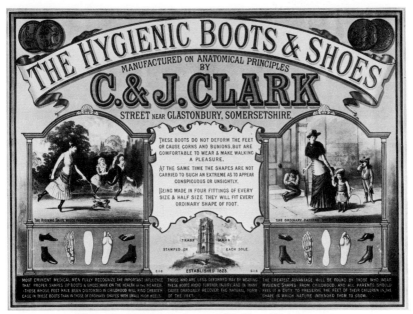

The spirit of the old Clarks exemplified by a Victorian poster

at a ratio of nine (children's) to six (women's) to one (men's), but they also knew that childhood memories had an important bearing on their adult sales.

To make matters worse, shoe manufacturers – like many other traditional British industries – were suffering from competition from overseas. At the top end of the shoe market, the Italians had long been acknowledged to have more flair than the British; their industry, clustered around villages and communities where shoe-making and designing somehow generated superlative talents, still dominates fashion shoes for both men and women. At the bottom end, much more ominously, Far-Eastern countries began to churn out shoes at prices so low that no British manufacturer could afford to compete. The oriental menace was soon followed by the Eastern Europeans who were able to move a bit further up-market and still undercut British prices.

From 1965 to 1975, Britain's shoe industry experienced its worst decade in living memory. Some 400 firms closed down, a third of all jobs disappeared, and profitability for the survivors dropped to a mere 3·7 per cent. And what affected Clarks in particular was the decline of care and concern to the point where many of their young customers came to regard them almost as two dirty words. Children came to associate the name of Clarks with parental discipline and fuddy-duddy attitudes. So prosperous did youth become (and so cheap the trendy shoes in the High Street) that they could go out and buy the platform heels or pointed toes made fashionable by the latest pop star or teenage idol, positively relishing the fact that the shoes – and the trend - would last for weeks rather than years, and that they were likely to damage rather than nurture their feet. It all went with dangerous living and rapidly passing fashions and fads.

There, in theory, could have perished the jobs of Clarks' 18,500 employees around the world. The 8000 inhabitants of Street (with no other industry apart from Millfield School to support them) could have faced economic disaster, and one could imagine marches organised to lobby Westminster and pleas for action against unfair foreign competition and for economic support. This is the background against which Clarks have had, since 1974, completely to reconsider their image, their place in the market, and perhaps even their attitude to care and concern.

In every respect, the Clarks' dilemma hinges on the subject of this book – design. Making shoes is not a highly skilled job; unlike weaving or the manufacture of specialist glass, shoemaking is a job that can be taught in a matter of weeks, and the Korean or Jugoslav from the countryside can be as effective a worker in this industry as a British secondary school-leaver. Britain is not particularly well placed to receive raw materials at a premium price. Our labour costs are higher than those of most of our competitors. Our market is in no way protected or favourably disposed towards home manufacturers. Apart from maintaining more efficient supply lines, the only way in which our manufacturers can sell shoes in Britain is by a close understanding of the market they serve and by designing shoes particularly suited to that market in terms of price and styling. Marketing and design are the main activities in which we can hope to defeat the opposition, and if we fail, then there are 73,000 more jobs – many of them in areas that depend totally on their shoe manufacturers – which could be lost.

Design in the shoe industry is not a single-faceted activity. At the very outset of the production process it is a designer who (in close collaboration with the marketing team) decides what shape the shoes should be; it is another designer who, at the other end of the chain, creates the point-of-sale image – the environment in which the shoe will be bought. Between these two designers there are others working on advertising, on production machinery and the rest, but for the purposes of this chapter the two extremes of design activity will serve very well, particularly because Clarks chose, in their crisis year, to separate these two design functions still further by retaining their 'in-house' designers to create the styling of their shoes, but by placing their corporate image in the hands of one of Britain's most adventurous design groups, Pentagram.

Very few of the shops that sold Clarks shoes took their instructions from Clarks. Most of them did not even belong to Clarks; in this respect the private company differed from the Sears-controlled British Shoe Corporation, which owned and operated most of the High Street multiples. And those that were owned by Clarks paid little obvious attention to the fact! Ravel, for example, did not even stock Clarks shoes, while Peter Lord went out of its way not to brandish the corporate image of the owner and sold shoes manufactured by Clarks' rivals as well as those made in Street. Pentagram took on a decidedly complex task: virtually that of designing showrooms for shops that were by no means committed to using Clarks' designs, and which had to pay for the privilege of adapting to any new scheme, while at the same time having no control whatsoever over the range of shoes that the 'point-of-sale' image was intended to promote! Clarks chose Pentagram because they were impressed by the grasp Pentagram's John McConnell displayed of marketing strategy. One wonders whether John McConnell really understood the slippery nature of the operation he was about to undertake.

Take Mrs Merley. Mrs Merley owned a small shoe shop in Pittshanger Lane in North Ealing, a middle-class suburb on the Western fringes of London. Her premises were tiny; the walls of the shop itself were filled from floor to ceiling with shoe boxes, and she had a tiny store-room at the back that held her overflow stock, which also lined the cramped stairs to her upstairs flat. The mothers of Ealing and of other suburbs for miles around brought their children to the shop in the knowledge that no child would leave it without the proprietress herself inspecting the fit of the shoes they purchased. Her two assistants (a sister and her niece) were not unskilled at fitting shoes, but it was Mrs Merley herself – a kindly, elderly lady – who had been trained in care and concern, and she knew her small clients and their feet and the erratic behaviour of both.

Mrs Merley's shop was replicated up and down Britain; there were around 2000 small independent traders not unlike her. They did not stock only Clarks shoes: K Shoes and Start-Rite were rivals for this corner of the market, while many smaller shops were having to come to terms with the changing market by stocking the fast-moving, often ill-fitting ranges that customers were demanding. Mrs Merley represented care and concern, but she also personified the crunch that confronted Clarks.

There was no immediate crisis facing her shop: the suburb she served was a prosperous one and packed with 'sensible' mothers determined that their children should get the best and only the best. She and her two relatives gave no obvious signs that they cared about large profits, but one could not imagine that their margins were very high, and their throughput was by no means as great as that of the multiples and the department stores with their shoe sections staffed, very often, by virtually untrained girls who did not stay around long enough to learn much about feet. To whom were Clarks and Pentagram to pay more attention? Along they came to Mrs Merley, anxious to persuade her to move a little further 'into the 1980s' and to branch into more fashionable shoes to entice the older children and the fashion-conscious youngsters. First she looked at Clarks' new catalogue with its shoes designed for 11 and 12-year-olds, but with high heels and flimsy support straps. 'I won't touch them', said Mrs Merley, and selected her purchases from the austere, traditional end of the list. Then she looked at the catalogue of wall displays and shoe stands which the trendy designers from Pentagram wanted her to buy and install in her shop. 'I don't like them', said Mrs M. 'I can't afford them, and if I could, where could I fit them? I simply don't have that kind of space.' Remember Mrs Merley; her spirit hangs heavily over Clarks' attempts to move into new markets.

Of course, the other retailers presented a different kind of problem. There was difficulty, in days of rapid staff turnover, in persuading them to send even one supervisor down to Street for that vital care and concern training session. There was the problem of persuading them to favour the house style designed by

Mrs Merley's 'traditional' shoe shop . . .

Pentagram to bring the Clarks' image to the attention of clients: why should they do Clarks that kind of favour? Their store almost certainly had its own house style: would the Pentagram designs fit in with this image? Would they dominate it or clash with it? Perhaps in some cases they were actively afraid of promoting Clarks: remember the movement away from parental discipline and all that went with it?

This, then, was the problem facing John McConnell of Pentagram. On the one hand, a very mixed bunch of retailers whom he had to persuade to buy the Clarks' scheme. On the other, a shoe manufacturer with a Quaker tradition of care and concern, a dislike of ostentation, and with a range of shoes neither as stylish as the Italians nor as faddish as other imported styles. The very emblem of Clarks reflected their conservatism: it was the copper-plate signature of one of the two founders, James Clark, who had lived from 1811 to 1906 and who, with Cyrus (1801 to 1866), had seen the company grow from a cottage industry.

McConnell's first move was a bold one. That signature on the end of the tastefully hued green boxes was the aspect of Clarks the majority of consumers saw most often. In shops like Mrs Merley's, the shoe boxes lined the walls with the labels on display so that assistants could spot the style and size. To McConnell, both the colour and the signature could do with being livened up. The signature he redesigned, not radically but recognisably, by thickening it out and colouring it primary yellow. The colour of

... and Pentagram's bright new image for a children's shoe shop

37

the boxes he changed to a much brighter green. The box-end labels were also gingered up considerably. At a stroke, the shoe buyers of Britain could be informed that things were waking up at Clarks. It was Philip Hammersley, manager of the children's division and one of the new generation of young, non-family executives who had been given responsibility for Clarks' 'new wave', who informed the Board of McConnell's suggestion. The reception was one of astonishment. What Pentagram were proposing was the demolition of the tradition of a century – that's how long the man's signature had been carrying the company's image to every corner of Britain. As to their choice of colours, well, even for those who liked them, there remained the fact that all Clarks' trucks were painted in the old green, and that 1½ million pairs of shoes were at that moment sitting in boxes of the old hue which nobody could afford to throw away. The introduction of a new colour would inevitably create a mottled effect, while old and new liveries clashed with each other on the shelves. The debate was long and animated, and history doesn't relate just how Philip Hammersley won the day, but he did. The children's division is now converted to the new colours and the new graphic style.

McConnell's next suggestions tended to enhance the old traditions rather than challenge them. The care and concern elements were forcefully grasped and pulled to the forefront of Clarks' sales drive. A new carrier bag, for instance, carried the full message: 'Children's feet need room in a shoe to grow properly. A Clarks' trained fitter using the Clarks' footgauge to measure both feet for length and width can tell you which shoe size gives the right amount of room for growth. The correct width is as important as the correct length.' And prominent on the same display was a picture of the footgauge, which was also featured on posters, wall displays, and in a 1930s-style lapel badge given only to those assistants who had been down to Clarks for their shoe fitting course. The footgauge itself was now housed in a brightly coloured new fitting stool, with the updated yellow signature boldly reminding the customers whose patronage was bringing them this special service. The bright colours of the footstool were matched by a range of customer chairs and shoe stands, with triangular mirrors on the back of which were pictorial panels featuring a shoe complete with enormous shoe-lace so that waiting children could play and practise tying up their laces. There was an additional range of wall panels, not directly connected with Clarks or even with shoes, but designed to catch the attention of children in the queue and to establish in their minds that Clarks could be associated with fun, fitting footprints to various wild animals, or emblems to football teams. These were accompanied by hand-outs of literature, make-your-own kits and

Care and concern on Pentagram's carrier bag

so on . . . and by now McConnell was in real danger of upsetting the traditionalists among the retailers. Mrs Merley, for instance, proclaimed that she didn't have space for these gimmicky placards; quite frankly she preferred the more austere approach. Nor would she swap her bentwood chairs for the garish Pentagram seats and mirrors. Others resisted for different reasons: their flowered wallpaper or muted decor would provide completely the wrong backing for the bold primary colours and shapes from Pentagram; it was asking too much of them that they should alter their decor for the sake of accommodating one supplier. Ironically, the chain whose colours were least suited to the new designs was the Clarks' subsidiary Peter Lord: their own design team had created a decor in brown and cream and there was no way that they would accommodate Clarks' new image!

Nonetheless there were successes. By July 1978 no fewer than 65 shops had been refitted to the Pentagram scheme, and the shop-fitting team was solidly booked. The children's division back at Street acknowledges that they too have been encouraged to move forward into bolder and brighter shoe designs to match their new point-of-sale image, and one of the happiest examples of co-operation between Pentagram and Clarks came from John McConnell's idea that shoe fittings should be emphasised in a way the young customer could appreciate. Young shoes were now sporting a plastic wedge in the arch of the foot; McConnell suggested that the wedges should be in different colours (primary of course) to help children to choose their own fitting. Hammersley's designers agreed, and it is now reckoned by all concerned to be an actual selling point among children that they are able to touch these wedges; that their fitting has become three dimensional and coloured. Pentagram, of course, backed this up with a series of display stands built up from much larger plastic wedges, so for the first time in the exercise the point-of-sale design came right back to the point of manufacture.

But Pentagram's experiences were by no means all as painless as this. In the men's division they had some success, echoing Clarks' successful 'chunky' casual range by using stark and stylish

Two versions of the new men's shoe display stand

slatted-angle shelving with a brushed metal surface. But their biggest opposition came when they tried to introduce a tiered, wedding-cake stand on which to display women's shoes. The idea behind this circular shelf unit was that Pentagram would supply a different slot-in backing every three months, so for the price of just one stand the shop would receive a different, colourful display four times a year. At the time of writing, this unit was finding favour neither among the Clarks' women's division nor among the retailers . . . and it highlights the difficulties faced by Pentagram, or any out-of-house design group, in their relations with their manufacturing client. Pentagram, inevitably, feel that they could achieve more if they could have more influence over the ranges of shoes they were hired to promote; they are also

The adaptable, but coolly received, tiered stand for women's shoes

frustrated by Clarks' lack of control of the retail outlets. Life would obviously be much easier if Clarks had their own named chain of shoe stores, but Clarks are most unlikely to take this step for the simple reason that no store can survive by selling just one brand, and what supplier would deliver to, or what customer shop at, a store carrying the name of a single manufacturer?

And if there are rumblings in the Paddington warehouse where Pentagram have their offices, there are murmurs of equal discontent down in Street, where the less glamorous work of designing and producing shoes is carried on by less highly paid, and in their own view more realistic, designers who really do know about shoes. Derek Radford, for instance, is the chief designer in the men's division of Clarks, and he has worked a long time for the firm. He is a native of Somerset, and a gentle man who is capable of cutting and stitching a shoe with the best of them – in fact, that's how he sets about designing a new range. Derek played a major part in Clarks' biggest leap forward in recent years, the introduction of Polyveldt shoes in the early 1970s. Through 1977 and 1978 he was engaged in what, for the men's division at least, represented an even more difficult move forward. He wouldn't, couldn't have been involved in either had he not been thoroughly familiar with every aspect of shoe manufacture.

The story of the Polyveldt shoe goes back to the early 1960s, when Clarks' R & D division – along with those of other shoe manufacturers – were experimenting with polyurethane as a possible light, cheap and flexible alternative to leather and particularly to crepe rubber for the soles of casual shoes. In 1962 they researched two chemicals that, when mixed together at the right temperature and injected into a mould, would expand to fill it completely. A minute later the polyurethane sole could be stripped out of the mould and another one injected. In the production technique a large mobile vat containing the two chemicals trundles up and down a line of moulds injecting the mixture into each one, while two operatives open and re-set the moulds. That, at any rate, is how it works today, but 10 years of expensive development work lay ahead of Clarks, and virtually all their competitors withdrew from the struggle. It was not until 1973 that Clarks produced their first polyurethane product – a woman's boot called the Contura – and as this book is written their patience and investment has paid off: they are selling their polyurethane technology all round the world.

Polyurethane soles saved the life of Clarks' men's division. Back in 1974 the men's division was trailing the other two segments of Clarks' output by the ratio mentioned before: one million pairs of men's shoes to six of women's and nine of children's. Most of these sales came from their rather characterless formal city shoes – and Clarks duly sold off the Northampton factory which made these – with only one lively performer among all their male output – the so-called Desert Boot. This casual, crepe-soled design had been introduced into the range when one of the less predictable members of the family, Nathan Clark, returned from India in 1948 proclaiming that this militaristic kind of footwear would catch on with a generation who still remembered active service and were likely to have more hours to devote to leisure, and he was right. The chunky, rugged design carved itself a hole in the market and occupied it for 20 years.

But by the early 1970s, the Desert Boot was on its way out. Clarks had spotted the need for a replacement, but this time for a shoe that would take full advantage of the new polyurethane injection moulding techniques. Derek Radford was encouraged to turn his attention to the properties offered by the new technology and to incorporate these into a new leisure shoe which, it was hoped, would boost the sagging fortunes of the men's division.

Polyurethane soles were light – much lighter than crepe rubber – and very flexible – a polyurethane sole could be bent right back

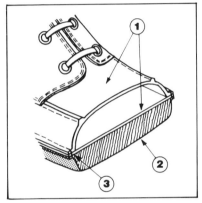

The innovatory construction of the Clarks Polyveldt
Special Polyveldt features are hide leather uppers and insole (1) firmly attached to a light,
durable polyurethane sole (2) by a stitched veldtschoen seam (3)

on itself – but the principal design benefit came from the very
exact shape to which polyurethane, unlike crepe or leather, could
be moulded. It was possible to produce a polyurethane sole with
a very thin horizontal lip, tapering away from a much thicker,
stronger sole, and Radford immediately spotted that here was an
opportunity to improve on the veldt technique of making shoes.
A veldt shoe has the upper part of the shoe, usually leather, joined
to the sole by welted stitches; with crepe or leather the sole had
to be relatively thick if the shoe was to be strong, so the welted
stitching was inevitably arduous and the result was a very heavy
piece of footwear. The Polyveldt, with its very narrow outer rim
and consequently simple stitches securing the upper firmly to the
sole, was an altogether different beast – an incredibly light shoe

that immediately caught on in the market-place. Fast on the trail of Polyveldt came Radford's second successful design, the Naturetrek; the idea here was to use as few pieces of leather and as little construction as possible in the making of the shoe, the result was a brutal Cornish pasty of a shoe that again caught the popular imagination. Within three years the sales of the men's division had risen to three million pairs compared with five million pairs of women's and eight of chilren's. The two successful men's shoes were duplicated for women and children as well, and their success played a significant part in helping Clarks to weather the slump.

But in the shoe industry nothing can be allowed to remain static. Sales of the Naturetrek and the Polyveldt were reckoned to be flattening out, and if Clarks were to maintain their market share, the men's division had to continue to expand. Apart from sports shoes (which were most cheaply manufactured in the Far East) the only alternative to introducing yet more casual shoes was to look at their old stamping ground, the city shoe. Despite having sold their Northampton factory, Clarks continued to buy from their old manufacturer and to maintain a presence in the formal shoe market, in the interests of maintaining a full range of footwear. Now, however, if expansion was to be the name of the game, something radical had to be done with city shoes.

Neville Gillebrand, manager of the men's division, together with Derek Radford and the Clarks' marketing team, spent 1977 and the first part of 1978 attempting to introduce polyurethane soles to city shoes, in the hope of persuading customers that all the advantages they brought to casual shoes could now be brought to formal footwear. As a design concept it was far from easy; polyurethane soles, up to that time, had been thick, chunky affairs because both the chemistry and the design of the moulds demanded it. It was not until 1977 that the chemists produced a mixture capable of producing the slender sole needed for men's shoes, and an uphill struggle still remained to design moulds that would turn out soles with no damaging bubbles in the polyurethane. On top of that, the shoe hadn't to *look* plastic: the upper had to be leather while the true nature of the sole was to be concealed as far as possible.

Radford went through no fewer than five different design prototypes before he could satisfy marketing, production and himself. In fact, he would have been happier with the penultimate design and few would have disagreed with him on the evidence of the beautiful shoe he himself stitched to demonstrate to his colleagues. The problem, as production manager Charles Fuidge soon discovered, was that the fourth design was so precise that it could not be sewn at the speeds required for mass production; it would quite simply be too expensive. Six months' work went into designing the final version, and on 13 January 1978 it was finally agreed by Neville Gillebrand and his colleagues that model number five was the one they should go for.

This left them just eight weeks to get a production version ready for the Harrogate Shoe Fair. This is the regular cycle of the shoe business and it applies, of course, to many other industries. At Harrogate all the manufacturers put their goods on display and the retailers arrive from all over the United Kingdom to view the new offerings. At the fair Clarks had to specify price, delivery volume and dates, and the kind of publicity back-up they would be providing for the new shoe.

On the surface, all looked well; the retailers appeared to give the Sidebinder (as the new shoe was now called) a good reception, while adding their two ha'porth of advice as to how the machining could be improved. The Clarks' team made encouraging noises

Examples of the polyurethane-soled Sidebinder city shoe

and noted that few of their products had in the past received quite such a warm welcome (the trade had positively turned its back on the Polyveldt when it first appeared). But underneath it all they were not a little worried by problems back in Street, where the production line was far from ready.

Harrogate also gave evidence of another set of design problems that had at that time far from worked themselves out. The experienced eye in search of Pentagram's presence in the lavish Clarks' display at Harrogate (instead of joining the other manufacturers in the exhibition hall, Clarks take a suite of reception rooms at the nearby Majestic Hotel) would have spotted only two McConnell designs. The wedges on the soles of the new children's shoes were there, together with the shelves Pentagram designed to go with them, and so were the slatted-angle shelf units carrying the existing men's range of Polyveldt and Naturetrek. But that was all.

Harrogate is a fixed point in the shoe manufacturer's year and one that he cannot afford to miss. Another spans the busy months of September and November, when retailers traditionally take in their first tentative stocks of new lines, watch how they sell, then frantically place new orders for the successful shoes. It was vital for Clarks to have the Sidebinder in the shops by September, and to be ready to meet what they hoped would be substantial fresh orders by November. By midsummer, things were not going at all well. The moulds needed for the new shoes did not arrive until far too late and it was 25 June before the production line first swung into action. Charles Fuidge at this stage was cheerful. 'If all goes well from now on,' he said, 'we'll meet our target.' Neville Gillebrand wasn't so sure. Something, he thought, was bound to go wrong with such a new design, and if they missed the deadlines, it would put them back for months. But even if, after this is written, the Sidebinder turns out to have missed the September cut-off, there is one other factor that could save the project. A fine September keeps men out of the shoe shops, and retailers delay their orders. For perhaps the first time, Clarks prayed for a fine September.

That would be in keeping with the rest of 1978, which was one of Clarks' best since the war. Children's shoes had a boom year: the wet summer kept sales of shoes, as opposed to sandals or trainers, at a high level. The country's relative prosperity kept the cash registers ringing, and – most significantly of all – there were indications that the new, slightly older generation of mothers was exhibiting just a little more care in their choice of shoes for their children. Pentagram were watching the trends as well: it would be ironical if a drive towards more aggressive sales methods were to be pre-empted by a change in the habits of the buying public. It will have been an intriguing year in the shoe industry, and one that illustrates just how important and controversial the designer's role can be at one moment, and how ephemeral it can seem at the next. But whatever the appearances, it is and always will be design that sells shoes; design linked to correct judgment of conditions in the market-place.

Chapter Three

The Run-Flat Tyre

A designer's moment of inspiration leads to a decade of
development, dedication and disappointment as the world's
most severe economic crisis coincides with Dunlop's attempt to
launch a new generation of car tyre

On 14 February 1970, Tom French was sitting in his first-class
seat on a British Airways flight from London Heathrow to Detroit
on one of the many flights which his company – Dunlop – had
instructed him to make from their headquarters at Fort Dunlop
to the car manufacturing centres of the world. His quest was for
the next major development in the design of car tyres.

As he sat, Tom French began to doodle on the paper tray mat
in front of him and to jot down his thoughts, in Russian. He had
spent some time in Russia and still regularly thought in Russian
and therefore wrote in that language; in any case, you never know
who might be sitting next to you in an aeroplane. ('It would have
been just my luck if my neighbour had turned out to be a Russian
automotive designer', says French today . . . but he wasn't.)

His doodles might, in any case, have turned out to be totally
unimportant; that's the way it is when a designer's mind begins to
stray into new territory. As it happened, they turned out to be
surely the most significant ever made on a British Airways napkin,
and perhaps the most ambitious drawings to be produced by the
tyre industry since the war.

'Start', he wrote in Russian, and drew a horizontal line. Then
another line to represent an empty tyre. Then, still in Russian,
'Air'. 'Tyre without air' came next, and then 'How to solve the
problem'.

Above the two lines he drew a shorter line to represent the
load; in a normal car, this would be at the hub of each of the four
wheels. 'Load will keep it in mesh', he wrote, and 'Tread must
carry load'. Seemingly, all he had done was to jot down a set of
naïve and self-evident observations. In fact, he knew that he now
had the key to an important discovery, and his next words in
Russian were: 'Could we have a patent?'

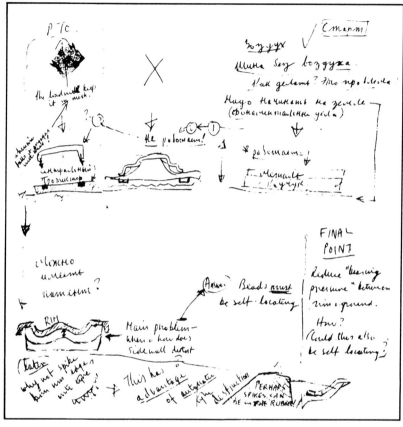

Tom French's napkin sketch that gave rise to the Dunlop run-flat tyre

Eight years and a few million pounds of Dunlop development money later, Tom French is asking himself whether that aeroplane journey might not have set him off on an exercise that was a prime example of 'design push' – a brilliant concept that had the misfortune to arrive ahead of its time, foisted by an over-eager company on a market that has so far failed to take advantage of its true significance. On the other hand, it may be that Tom French and Dunlop have given Britain a world lead in the third generation of vehicle tyres, and that Tom's doodles represent the most successful and inspired design of the decade. The next few years will tell.

The previous generation of car tyres had evolved a little more slowly. When Michelin took over the ailing Citroën company in the late 1930s, they had come face to face with the fact that fron wheel drive cars – assuredly the design of the future – presented tyre manufacturers with a problem in that the strain they put on their tyres was much greater than with rear wheel drive. Even before the war, Michelin had the idea of building a radial belt of steel into the carcase of the tyre to reinforce the rubber. This gave much greater strength than the earlier crossply tyre, but the first radials gave a very harsh and unpleasant ride, 'Turning', as the critics of the day put it, 'every car into a truck.'

The war hampered any progress with the new tyres, and it was not until 1948 that Michelin were able to build radial tyres in earnest for their own Citroën cars; it took a further five years before Lancia became the first outside car manufacturer to fit them. The rest is now history: into the 1960s the fashion for radials grew and grew; Michelin's rivals – including Dunlop – fought back as best they could, improving on the ride given by steel radials by using textile reinforcement instead, but Michelin never lost the lead they had established, and by 1977 almost every car on the road was fitted with radial tyres, so their market was a very large one.

It was the memory of Michelin's victory in the introduction of radials as much as anything else that prompted Dunlop to send Tom French on his travels to identify, or perhaps even to design, the next world-beater. After his flight, Tom checked in to the downtown Pontchartrain hotel and took out his pocket tape-recorder. His words are still on record:

'Clearly one of the key parts to this job is the sort of integrated redesign of the rim flange, the rim bearing surface of the tyre bead and lower sidewall, which can clearly be integrated in such a way as to force the beads into the corner of the bead seat and flange . . .

'One would think that with the right choice of the shape on the top of the flange and the way it engages with the tyre and of the materials used – frictional characteristics and so on – one can produce the sort of resultant force one wants and as the deflated tyre runs forward, continuously to screw itself into the corner . . .

'It is obvious that a low-ratio tyre is pretty well essential and one could easily consider going way below 60 in line with the 30s or even 20s of the race tyres we are now doing, which themselves are tending to develop into non-pneumatic tyre structures and then again, looking on the airless or nearly airless condition and extrapolating it backwards to the inflated condition – this appears worth giving some further thought to.'

The dictated memorandum, combined with the sketches he had made on the flight, set out Tom French's concept of the 'run-flat' tyre: a tyre that would never burst disastrously and throw a car out of control at high speeds, and which, after any kind of puncture, would still be good for at least another 100 miles of near-normal motoring at speeds of up to 50 mph. The tyre would offer, on the one hand, safety from accidents caused by punctures and, on the other, the assurance that the driver need never be late for a meeting because of a flat tyre.

This is the way Tom French's mind was working. The dramatic shredding of a punctured tyre is caused, not by the blow-out itself, but by the way the rubber of the tread is forced across the sharp edge of the wheel and cut to ribbons by the metal. Keep the wheel centred above the tread and maintain some form of cushioning, however slight, and there is a good chance that the tyre will run safely for some distance after the puncture.

The reason most tyres collapse at an angle is that the lower wall of the tyre, the bead seat, is positioned on the wheel flange and kept there simply by the force of the air inside the tyre and by the tight fit of the bead. Take away the air pressure and subject the tight-fitting bead to the chaotic stresses of a punctured tyre still travelling at speed, and the tyre bead seat will inevitably slide inwards towards the centre of the flange, leaving one side or other of the tread running helplessly under the vicious cutting edge of the wheel. It can then slip right into the fitting well in the wheel and be completely dislodged, leaving only metal grinding against the tarmac. If this happens at speed the driver is very likely to lose control of the car.

This is the problem to which Tom French had addressed himself. As his taped message has it: 'Should it in fact be directional, ie to produce a maximised sideforce and minimum circumferential longitudinal force?' The answer – equally obscured by jargon – was to 'locate the tyre bead seats positively'. The thought process was, in plain language, this. Any movement of the bead into the fitting well of the wheel would cause some kind of deflection of the tyre that would disrupt steering, perhaps fatally. The solution was to design a wheel that locked the bead firmly to the wheel under any circumstances. As luck would have it, French discovered that only one side of the tread in fact needed to be locked because the other rim remained stable enough not to cause steering problems. By the end of the summer of 1970, French's team at Fort Dunlop had designed and tested the first type of run-flat, the so-called 'crimped' tyre and wheel.

The next step was to prevent friction between metal and rubber inside the punctured tyre. What was needed was a cushion of air and at the same time some method of preventing heat from being generated. The team started research into lubricants that could be released at the instant a puncture occurred; these would serve two purposes in that a liquid lubricant could act as a sealant and prevent air escaping, while at the same time preventing friction.

The liquid was to be contained in small cylinders – dispensers – fixed by a wire harness to the rim of the wheel inside the tyre. At the moment of the puncture, the tyre would collapse and put pressure on the dispensers, valves would open and liquid would escape into the tyre to perform its twin jobs of sealing and lubricating. But tests threw up an unexpected bonus. The design team had set themselves fairly modest performance targets: 30 mph for 30 miles after the puncture. The early tests were, in the manner of such experiments, performed with a variety of liquids and at a variety of speeds. One wheel, which was being run with a simple water-based lubricant, ran flat for some distance, and then surprised everybody by actually increasing its pressure! What was happening was that the heat inside the tyre was turning the water of the lubricant into vapour, and this in turn partially re-inflated the tyre and prevented the collapsed sidewalls from rubbing on the inside of the tread. Of course, to do this the vapour had to be trapped somehow inside the punctured tyre.

The design team knew there were bound to be other lubricating liquids that would vapourise at lower temperatures than water and create more pressure; that was just a question of fresh research into the chemistry of lubricants. The more fundamental problem was to cash in on this piece of good fortune by sealing off the hole caused by the puncture through which the pressure would otherwise escape. Large blow-outs would obviously be

Early Dunlop press release pictures of the 'total mobility' tyre compared with a conventional type

beyond this kind of remedy, and punctures in the sidewall were also difficult to seal, but a survey commissioned by the Dunlop team revealed that well over three quarters of all punctures occurred in the centre of the tread, where self-sealing would in fact be relatively easy. The technique they devised was to place two chemical components inside the tyre which, when mixed, would form a seal. Inside the dispensers, ready to pass into the tyre at the moment it was deflated, was an alcohol-based fluid. The second compound was a stiff lubricant gel containing rubber particles (actually made from ground rubber from Dunlop's retread factories) and some synthetic fibres; the gel was coated round the inside of the tyre when it was being manufactured. When a puncture occurred, the alcohol compound immediately mixed with the gel on the tyre, diluting it into an oily fluid; the sealant then did its job of blocking off the hole while the fluid vapourised and created the magic cushion on which the wheel could float for distances and at speeds that Tom French and his team had never dreamt possible when they began.

The development of the lubricants and of the new tyre bead seating had been carried out at staggering speed, especially when compared with the time it took to bring the radial tyre from the drawing board onto the road, and the Dunlop team acknowledge the help they were given by the department of tribology at Leeds University. Between Tom French's plane journey to the day when Dunlop's (then) managing director John Simon first drove around in a Mini fitted with run-flat tyres lay just 18 months of intensive research and development. The design work did not by any means finish there – in many respects it had not finished when this book was being written – but the clarity and simplicity of Tom French's work had a tremendous momentum which survived the early months and permeated the whole project development.

Dunlop realised pretty quickly that they had a product they could manufacture; the big question was whether anyone would want to buy it. Marketing tyres is by no means as easy as selling toothpaste or television sets, or any other factory-direct-to-retailer product. Tyres arrive at showrooms accompanied, as often as not, by motor cars and the biggest (if not necessarily the most profitable) slice of the tyre market is the 'original equipment business' – namely, selling tyres to car manufacturers to be fitted to cars before they leave their factories. Dunlop in 1971 had a majority share of the OE market; they not only made the tyres but also the wheels for a large slice of the British market and about 80 per cent of the European one. It's a field in which precise figures are closely guarded, but there is no doubt that Dunlop's biggest single customer was their Midlands neighbour British Leyland, since Dunlop supplied the majority of Leyland's tyres and wheels. Doing business in this way leaves a relatively small profit margin on each tyre and wheel sold – the car industry is a tight one, and the manufacturers have a shrewd idea of their suppliers' costs and a tough attitude to negotiating prices – but if Dunlop did not make as much money per tyre out of OE as they did in the replacement market, at least the bulk orders from manufacturers gave them a precise idea of how many sets of tyres and wheels they should manufacture, and they could gear their production accordingly. The run-flat was, of course, to be an original equipment concept – a driver can't fit one run-flat tyre as a spare with a kit of conventional tyres – but more of that later.

If Dunlop were to make a success of their new design of tyre they had first to persuade British Leyland and the other car makers that there would be a market – that the public would be prepared to pay extra for the run-flat. In a sense, they had to carry out the market research for a product that they did not themselves sell – a car fitted with the new tyres. If the customer was not convinced, then the car manufacturers were unlikely to buy the new tyre; for Dunlop, it amounted to a marketing operation at one remove from the High Street. Onto the scene at this point arrived Iain Mills, who was to become a moving force in the development of run-flat tyres, Marketing Planning Manager by title but very much partner to Tom French and continual champion of the run-flat project. Iain Mills's first job was to identify which cars the run-flat tyre would be most likely to suit. Jaguar had always favoured 'low-profile' tyres and (harking back to Tom French's original memorandum) the run-flat was likely to be wide and fat and good at hugging the road. The Rover group were keen to project their solid image of safety and reliability, and these were the main claims French made for his design. Porsche had been the first to buy Dunlop's textile radials, and it was possible that their fancy for speed and performance would be tickled by a tyre that could not be stopped by a puncture. Family cars, at this stage, had been ruled out as a possibility because the team believed that the new tyre would be too expensive for the low-margin mass market.

Iain Mills' first market survey surprised Dunlop management. Motorists, it appeared, were acutely aware of the *inconvenience* caused by punctures – a family motorist could expect to have a puncture every 16,800 miles on average, and at least half of the drivers (the women vocal amongst them) regarded these punctures as a considerable liability. *Safety*, on the other hand, took a back seat in the public awareness in 1971; seat-belts and laminated windscreens were receiving a frosty reception at that time, and people in Britain did not appear to be prepared to pay extra to avoid accidents that they believed would never happen to them.

This convinced Mills that Dunlop should not concentrate their sales pitch solely on the high-performance, and hence endangered, motorist, but also on the housewife in the prosperous family's second car, who would be a strong candidate for a tyre that would save her the embarrassment and discomfort of standing at the side of the road waiting for someone to help her change a wheel. On the evidence the Dunlop Board agreed that the run-flat tyre should be launched as soon as possible, with a strong marketing drive directed both at expensive large cars of the sort executives drive ('You need never miss an appointment . . .') and at smaller cars of the kind used by housewives. In November 1971 the Managing Director gave the go-ahead for full development of Tom French's design.

Another key personality had by now entered the inner circle of the run-flat project. John Murphy was a corporate planner with Dunlop and had joined the team preparing to launch the new tyre. The others pay tribute to his ability to wheel and deal with top management, and as often as not it was Murphy who saw the major decisions through the Dunlop management processes and got them accepted by the Board. At that time French, Mills and Murphy faced an extremely difficult marketing problem. To convince the motor manufacturers that they should buy the new tyre, they had to persuade the public. To convince the public, they had to demonstrate the tyre to the press in the hope that the press would write about it and create a market pull that would satisfy the motor men that the tyre should be fitted to new models. But if Dunlop demonstrated the tyre to one branch of the press, they ran the risk of upsetting other journalists who would feel they had been left out of an 'exclusive'. Likewise with the makers: to whom should they show the tyre first? The manufacturers didn't want to read about it in the papers; they all wanted to see it for themselves, and everyone wanted to be the first to see it. How could the three men possibly meet all these requirements simultaneously?

Terrified of an unauthorised leak, and relying very heavily on the discretion of all concerned, Mills, French and Murphy set about planning one of the most formidable launching ceremonies ever arranged for a new product. They divided their target audience into three categories: the motor manufacturers of the world; the media; and, finally, the opinion formers (legislators, lobbyists and pressure groups, motoring organisations and so forth). Within days of the official decision to go ahead with the run-flat, Iain Mills had shaped his plan for his mammoth sales-cum-publicity jamboree.

First came a strictly trade session. Amid winter gales at the Motor Industries Research Association track at Nuneaton in

Warwickshire, the boards and senior managements were shipped in, first of British Leyland, then of Ford UK, Ford Europe, Chrysler UK and Chrysler USA, Mercedes-Benz and Volkswagen (the Germans were met off their flight by no fewer than eight Daimlers – they had made it clear that they expected as much). Each manufacturer was shown the run-flat tyre fitted to their own make of car, and left in no doubt that their rivals were being given a similar demonstration. They were encouraged to drive one-inch nails right into the tread and then to compare the ride with the way the car handled beforehand. Some were allowed to press the dramatic 'blow-out' button which, at speed, detonated a small charge in the tyre and simulated the worst that could befall a car.

An intrepid tester simulates a high-speed blow-out

They were reported to be impressed by the very small change that occurred in the car's handling. Then, once more in conditions of utter secrecy, the delegations were ushered back into their cars, the overseas visitors onto their chartered flights, and dispatched to their homes.

Christmas of 1971 was not very festive for Iain Mills, John Murphy and Tom French. It was spent at French's home planning the second and much bigger launch of the tyre, this time to introduce it to the press of the world, to the rest of the European car makers, and to the 'men of influence' whose support they believed they would need. More than ever they were worried about the risk of an unauthorised leak to the press of one country, which would blow the whole publicity campaign throughout the world. They were also concerned that individual manufacturers would be miffed that they were not getting privileged treatment while their competitors were. Every detail of the planning, every invitation that was sent out, was geared to this sensitive issue of priorities and embargoes.

The great launch started in February 1972 at the Paul Ricard racing circuit in the South of France. First came the French manufacturers, followed by the British press, then their German, Italian, French and Scandinavian colleagues. Each team was given the same treatment as the motor moguls had received at Nuneaton: 37 different car models from 15 manufacturers were available, fitted with run-flat tyres, for the visitors to handle and to test. The circuit resounded to the screech of tyres being put through their paces by the correspondents interspersed with the occasional loud report as another journalist took his life in his hands and tested the blow-out simulation at high speed.

The Dunlop demonstration team and their test cars

And the press launch had not happened a moment too soon: on the day the Italians (notoriously huffy about their right to privileged treatment) arrived, the story was broken back in Britain by a journalist on the *Guardian*. By the strict rules of Fleet Street he had not broken any embargo because he was not a motoring correspondent and had not been invited to the Paul Ricard circuit; he had come across the news of the run-flat tyre by following up a small gossipy story in Dunlop's neighbourhood newspaper, the *Birmingham Post*. Nothing, as it happened, was seriously affected; the Italians filed their story in time, but it proved how right Dunlop had been in hastening the launch.

So far, then, Dunlop's luck was holding. With the news well and truly broken – and all the correspondents who had visited the circuit gave the new tyre a very favourable reception – the travelling circus moved on to Italy and Pizzola, the test track owned by Dunlop's partners in tyres, Pirelli. Here the Italian manufacturers were at last given their chance to test the tyre about which they had read in their newspapers, and if there had been doubts that the last in line might have resented the fact, they were partly dispelled by the evident interest the Fiat team showed in the run-flat tyre. The final stage was a journey back to Paul Ricard to show the tyre to category three, the 'opinion-formers', who included Marcus Jacobson of the Automobile Association, the Hon G Lascelles, President of the Institute of Motor Industries, and the Chairman of the Royal Society for the Prevention of Accidents, together with a Birmingham professor who specialised in the study of motor accidents, the Royal Safety Institution, the Armed Forces ('The place was crawling with generals', remarks Tom French today) and, most important of all, the Men from the Ministry, headed by the Permanent Secretary of the Department of the Environment's Ministry of Transport.

The importance of the civil servants lay in the simple but awkward fact that the run-flat tyre was, in Britain, illegal. A recently passed Act had enjoined that tyres when being driven should at all times be inflated according to the manufacturer's specifications, which was a pretty sensible law for conventional tyres, but eliminated the main advantage of the new tyre which was, of course, the facility to motor on for at least another 100 miles with the tyre deflated to a very different pressure from the one at which it was designed ideally to operate! It took 18 months – which is blindingly fast by legislative standards – to get the law in Britain amended to accommodate the run-flat tyre. The amendment was, in fact, passed just in time for the tyre's official launch at the 1973 Motor Show at London's Earls Court.

What else did the European jamboree achieve, apart from adding many years to the ages of Mills, Murphy and French? Disappointingly, only two potential customers emerged showing real interest in the new tyre. One was Spen King, and it could be argued that, as British Leyland's chief designer, he would have been won over by much less expensive means than Dunlop had employed; after all, he worked just down the road from Fort

Dunlop and had always been professionally very close to Tom French. King and his then managing director, George Turnbull, had been interested in the run-flat from the very first for the simple reason that the concept eliminated the need for cars to carry a fifth, spare tyre. The P6B Rover, then the pride of Spen King's stable, suffered from a boot so small that it let down the rest of the car's luxurious design, and the thought of using that much extra space for luggage, linked to the safety and the 'no appointments missed through punctures' angles, added up to a telling argument for fitting the run-flat to the Rover. The Mini 1275GT, then coming on strong as a second car in a well-to-do two-car family, was another candidate, the angle this time being the seductive line about 'the end of the motorway nightmare' and the image of a helpless woman stranded in the rain with heavy traffic pounding past, heedless of her inability to change the punctured wheel. But, and it was a big but, on neither car did Leyland agree to fit the new tyre as an automatic fixture; it came as an optional extra costing £40 (in 1973) on the Rover and £30 on the Mini GT.

The other interested party was Fiat, following up their early show of interest at Pizzola. It took longer for them to follow through – it was not until 1976 that their 131 and the tiny 126 were offered with Dunlop's run-flat tyre – and again, they would not agree to make the tyre a standard fitting.

There had, of course, been a number of near misses. Ford are believed to have come within a whisker of choosing the tyre for their AVO Escort, but a characteristic cost-cutting exercise eliminated it from their plans at the last moment. Two years later, Ford again considered it seriously for their new Fiesta, and this would indeed have been a major breakthrough for Dunlop. There were bitter wrangles about the price – Ford are quoted as estimating the extra cost of fitting tyres and wheels, and adapting the suspension and the steering, at around £100; Mills and French swear that only minimal changes would have been needed to the suspension and that £40 would easily have covered them. As always, the client had the last say.

Disappointed, but still backed by an enthusiastic board, the three men began to prepare to manufacture the tyre, which up to then had been made by hand for each demonstration car. In an industry that normally takes a full year to gear itself up for the smallest variations in tread or tyre size it must have seemed hugely ambitious to allow just a year to establish a production line for a radically new wheel and tyre, especially bearing in mind that they were about to embark on an important change in the fundamental design.

Iain Mills had been running a series of 'mini-Ricards' –

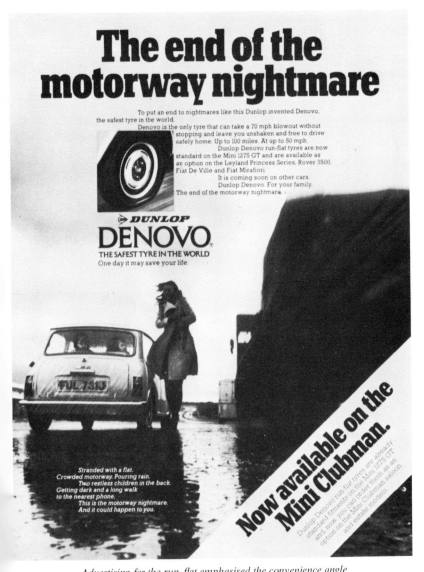

Advertising for the run-flat emphasised the convenience angle

promotions up and down Britain ('We found disused aerodromes which even the locals had forgotten were there') to which motor and tyre dealers were invited and at which discussions about the tyre were encouraged. One message was coming over loud and clear: the dealers objected to the fact that a tyre that had punctured and had been driven to a garage or tyre service depot had then to be cut off and replaced by an entirely new wheel. The crimped wheel seemed to the traders to be a terribly wasteful concept in a world beginning to worry desperately about conserving its resources.

Tom French went back to the Dunlop wheel design team and together they produced a fresh design for the wheel, consisting of three parts. The first section was an outer flange that could be taken off by removing eight bolts. The beads could then be removed, and the tyre itself could either be thrown away or repaired, according to its condition. The second part of the new wheel was an inner flange which in turn held the third part in position; this was a harness holding the cylinders of lubricant. The individual canisters could be replaced in the harness which could then be set back in position on the inner flange followed by a new or repaired tyre and the outer flange. The whole process took a trained mechanic with the correct tools about 20 minutes to perform, and this brings us to one of the biggest marketing jobs of all.

A hundred miles may seem a long way to be able to travel with a punctured tyre, but draw a number of 100-mile lines on a map starting from a single spot – any spot – and you can see that to provide service stations for a motorist with the promise that he need never deviate substantially *from his chosen route*, there are

an awful lot of 100-mile lines on which there have to be tyre-change facilities. The driver who has paid extra money for the run-flat concept isn't going to be happy if he has to travel 100 miles in the wrong direction to find a dealer equipped to repair the tyre, and the problem of setting up a chain of service stations to meet this challenge sent Iain Mills back to his computer to feed it with dozens of studies of the motoring habits of the Great British Public.

The calculations told Mills that he would need to establish a large number of dealers near motorway exits, in London, and in the industrial complexes of the Midlands and the North, as well, of course, as a fair sprinkling in the rest of the United Kingdom. He could not promise dealers at this stage that their investment in training and special equipment would be rewarded instantly by dramatic profits – with only two models sporting the wheel, this would have been hopelessly ingenuous – but he could suggest that if they came first into the business they would emerge in time as the established experts in run-flat tyres. A number of dealers did volunteer and training started in earnest in the spring of 1973. By the tyre's launch in October of that year there were 620 equipped and qualified dealers; by January 1978 there were 750, yet drivers were still heard to complain quite frequently that the depots were too few and far between for their convenience.

The same problem arose, of course, in Europe. People who drove Rovers or Mini GTs could afford to travel abroad in their cars, and the two Fiat models sold throughout the Continent. So here too Dunlop had to provide service support for users of their tyres, and although they claim that you never have to go more than 100 miles to a depot, even in Europe, the chances of being able to travel that distance *in the direction you want to go* are higher in West Germany and France than in any other countries.

Service back-up proved to be a nagging problem; few designers have to watch their work causing repercussions that continue for years after the product is 'up and running'. The next challenge, however, was and is common to a number of new designs: it's been accepted, we've set up a production line, we've even sold it, but what are we going to call it?

That 1973 Motor Show was looming large, and the run-flat tyre had to be christened or the launch would be – to put it mildly – a bit lame. Tom French and his team had got used to calling it the Total Mobility Tyre – they still have a slight hankering after the name – but someone pointed out gently that it didn't translate too well into other languages, German for instance. So, one autumn lunchtime, 100 or so sales managers from all Dunlop's European offices were called to the Overseas Club in London to suggest titles, and to criticise one another's suggestions. Iain Mills describes the event as resembling something between the United Nations on a bad day and the outbreak of World War Three: it was no time at all before national pride was being bruited far more loudly than any common interest in Dunlop. From the French came Stabifort or Secure; from the German contingent, Autorun or Ultimax; from the British, Lifeguard, Runsafe . . . and if countries seem to have produced suggestions in keeping with national characteristics, then all were excelled by the Italian contingent with Dunlopaprima and Verrissimo!

By the time each delegation had finished telling the others how awful their suggestions would be when translated into other languages, the meeting broke up in disarray. Bloodied and slightly bowed, John Murphy was despatched to tell Managing Director John Simon the bad news. Purposefully, John Simon strode to the window and gazed out. 'I have the answer,' he announced, in a moment almost as awful as the one when the chairman decides that he himself is just the man to appear in the company's television commercial; 'We'll call it Dunloflat.' Murphy retired to break the news to the others, but before they had worked out how to save the MD from unconsciously dubbing their prize product the 'Dunloflop', John Simon had another brainwave. At their next meeting, he waxed eloquent on the subject of worker participation and then suggested an offer of £100 to the member of staff who could suggest a good name.

The suggestion was good for shop-floor morale, but bad for results, although some of the suggested names were in fact a step up from previous rounds. Jack the Gripper, Natty Flatter, Revolution, and Flatypus were just four of the thousand or more that rolled in. With only a month to go, Murphy approached the Paris-based firm of consultants, Novamark. In two weeks, back came their short-list – Domino, Denovo, Dunovo and Allegra (both Dunlop and the agency were unaware at the time that Leyland were working on a car of almost the same name). The Board quickly approved the second name on the list, and the Denovo tyre was born. In September of 1973 the £2-million production line began to roll, and in October of that year the Denovo met its buying public for the first time at the Earls Court Motor Show.

Something else happened that October. The economies of the world were turned upside down by the Yom Kippur war and the dramatic rise in oil prices that resulted from it. The crisis had one lesser effect on the new tyre, in that road accidents were for a while reduced by new low speed limits, with the result that safety became a less important sales pitch – but there was also the crucial effect that car sales were slashed and the motoring world immediately became very cost-conscious indeed. In short, it wa the worst possible time to launch a new and relatively expensive prestige product.

What added to Dunlop's difficulties was the fact that the Denovo suffered the fate of any innovation in that it was plagued with rumours and criticisms. The new dealer network was said to be less than adequate once one strayed away from the main conurbations. The wide tyre was said to be heavy to drive and to need power-assisted steering, and this did nothing to endear it to the makers of such budget cars as the Ford Fiesta. The Denovo also acquired a reputation for being a noisy tyre. Finally, although the sidewalls were heavily reinforced, the centre of the tread was observed to wear away more rapidly than that of other tyres, and this meant early replacement and an additional expense in an already depressed market. For the next few years the 'second-round' manufacturers, who had planned to wait and watch how the motoring public would take to the new tyre, decided to remain firmly on the sidelines taking no action at all. Most important of all, the American manufacturers in Detroit showed no glimmer of interest. It looked as though a brilliant concept was in danger of perishing as the result of unfortunate timing, the industry's resistance to innovation, and the inevitable bugs and glitches that face any radically new product when it first arrives on the market.

Tom French and Iain Mills did not take the situation lying down. French attacked each of the design problems head on. Noise, for instance, was something of a poser until a remarkable piece of technological sleuthing traced the source of the complaint to – of all things – the pillars of the Rover windscreen. The tread pattern of the Denovo just happened to set off a reverberation in these pillars which – in the case of the Rover – was amplified by the car's scuttle. Solution: change the tread pattern and check its resonance.

The wear of the tyre occurred simply because – going back to Tom French's original concept – the Denovo was a wider, flatter tyre and it tended to balloon outwards if the car was not loaded at the back, especially if the driver put his foot down. This tended to scuff the centre of the tread on the rear wheels. French turned to Dunlop's older 'Aquajet' design of tread, in which more rubber came into contact with the road and therefore less stress was carried by the ribs of the pattern. He also introduced a different rubber compound for the tread.

As to the heavy steering, the solution varied from car to car. With the Rover, they modified the steel cord angles; in other cars the belt cord itself had to be adjusted (easier, because it was fabric). Iain Mills announced these modifications in late 1977 and when this book was written it was still too early to tell whether they would be enough to improve the very, very slow growth of demand for the Denovo. The Leyland Princess joined the range of Leyland cars on which the run-flat was available as an optional extra, and the Mini Clubman was given the tyre as a standard fitting – the first and as yet the only car to be so equipped. Mills predicts that six per cent of British tyres will be Denovos by the end of 1979, but he remains convinced that the swing upwards will come in time. John Murphy has left Dunlop to join the consultants Novamark, as Managing Director of their UK subsidiary.

French and Mills are not admitting defeat, not by any means. For one thing, they are hopeful that safety legislation combined with the need to reduce weight will force American makers to abolish the spare wheel and adopt the four-wheel concept. The year in which the law takes effect is 1980, and Mills points out that executives at both Ford and General Motors have stated that the Denovo is the leading contender in this field. At least 200 lbs must be saved in small and compact cars, and the spare wheel represents 50 lbs of unneeded weight. But the American tyre people are not standing still. A flurry of new designs have come from Goodyear, Firestone and Goodrich, some of them remarkably similar to the Denovo in design; some of them designed to carry the car for much shorter distances on what amounts virtually to a slender motorcycle wheel. The contest seems to be well and truly under way, and there is every chance that it may end up with patent rights disputed in court, or with Dunlop licensing their design to an American manufacturer. As Mills admits, Dunlop is hardly a household name in the USA, and the company would be competing in a big and somewhat rough league.

Then there is Japan, with crowded roads and scarcely a hard shoulder in sight. A single puncture can cause an entire city to seize up in the rush hour, and Dunlop are working closely with Sumitomo on the possibility that the Denovo could be marketed to ease Japan's chronic road congestion.

Meanwhile, back at Fort Dunlop, Tom French is by no means convinced that the design of the Denovo has reached its final evolution. For one thing, he believes that his original design – the crimped wheel – will come back into favour when the fad (as he sees it) for recycling passes away. Both he and Iain Mills have devoted the whole of the 1970s to the Denovo tyre; they are prepared to wait for a while and let the rest of the world catch up with them.

Chapter Four

When the Bubbles Burst

The best laid plans . . . or the failure of ICI, Britain's most
prestigious chemicals company, to launch a revolutionary
product onto, for them, an unfamiliar market

The challenge, on the face of it, looked pretty straightforward, how to package drinks in such a way that the fizz did not seep out using a material – plastics – that suffered none of the disadvantages of the traditional containers, glass bottles or metal cans. For a company as sophisticated as ICI, with a well deserved reputation throughout the world for their innovation in plastics and other petrochemical products, entry into the packaging business must have seemed a very small and natural step, and back in 1966 they decided to launch themselves into this field in the confidence that they could produce a unique package that would give them a foothold in a new and potentially profitable line of business. When they closed down their Merolite plants in 1977, ICI's managers ruefully admitted to themselves that some very complicated things happen on the way to the High Street.

It all started as a classic example of technology push. The Plastics Division of ICI, based at Welwyn Garden City, had set up a special 'Packaging Development Group' with the express task of looking for a corner of the market that did not, as yet, make any use of ICI's flexible plastics films, but into which they could move. It soon appeared that there were two possible target zones: the commonplace food can – the most usual container for baked beans, processed fruits and, at that time, soups, vegetables and so on – and the 'carbonated' drinks container. The temptations of the latter were powerful: it was a huge and growing business (it was to be worth £250 million a year by the mid-1970s) with sizeable rewards once a foothold had been secured. In addition there were growing lobbies voicing the disadvantages of the existing materials and it seemed that plastics could avoid most of the major difficulties of glass and cans, which were difficult to dispose of (plastics can be easily burnt) and can be dangerous –

witness feet cut by rusty cans or broken bottles (flexible plastics are virtually harmless). Furthermore, bottles and cans are heavy and cumbersome even when empty; plastics are not only light but they occupy almost no space until they are filled. Environmental groups throughout the world were clamouring for action to ban one-trip bottles, and there seemed to be every chance that this would lead to legislation to restrict the use of non-returnable containers and in turn tip the economic balance away from conventional packaging and open the door to a more acceptable method. In any case, the ICI scientists at Welwyn were on the look-out for new uses for their plastics, and this seemed the most natural course to follow.

The result was a 'pouch made from a seamless tube of biaxially oriented polyethylene terephthalate film, coated on the outside with a vinyidene chloride copolymer barrier resin . . .' or, in the market-place, the Merolite pouch. The first problem facing the researchers had been to produce a plastics film strong enough to hold the '4·2 atmospheres of carbonation' that Schweppes and Coca-Cola, among others, insisted were needed to add enough sparkle to attract the consumer. That's where the barrier resin came in, and if the ICI scientists never quite managed to achieve the ideal level, they did manage to produce a film capable of holding 3·8 atmospheres, which was enough for many soft drinks and for all beers. Their film had to be strong enough to withstand the rough handling it would inevitably receive from the delivery man, the supermarket assistant, and eventually the customer, and in this ICI were triumphant: we drove an MGB sports car over a filled pouch and it didn't leak in the slightest. It also had to be completely flavourless, since customers were apt to believe that plastics affected the taste of their drink, and in this respect too ICI's market surveys indicated that, even after weeks of storage, consumers could not detect a change in the flavour of drinks stored in Merolite pouches. On a more subjective level, however, there continued to be resistance to the concept of storing drinks such as beer in plastics. As the French put it, beer was 'too noble' a drink for this form of packaging!

So far, so good. Next, what shape was the package to be? ICI certainly considered the possibility of making a conventional, bottle-shaped container from rigid plastics, much like the cordial bottles commonly available, but – inevitably – made of their heavier plastics in order to contain the fizz. They soon dismissed this idea, either because it didn't match their original concept of finding new uses for their flexible films, or for the more sophisti-cated reason that almost any plastics manufacturer could (and subsequently did) produce a rigid bottle, but only ICI would be adventurous enough to leap two steps ahead and take a clear lead

Merolite soft-drink tubes and packaging

in the race towards new containers. Film, in any case, met the prime requirement of designing in plastics in that it made it possible to produce a shape that required the smallest amount of material, and on the scale of production ICI anticipated, with ever-rising prices of oil-based products, this saving in materials could prove vital. The rest was pure physics: the 'seamless tube' was the most economical use of film to package the required amount of drink. It also raised the first of what was to be a long list of major problems besetting the new project.

The tube was, to many consumers, not very attractive; market surveys later proved that the first-time sale of Merolite was in fact very difficult. The tube was not easy to place on display on supermarket shelves because its most natural position was horizontal; it was also difficult to stack in the bottle rack of the average refrigerator. Drinking was tricky because there wasn't a firm lip around which to curve the mouth. After a few weeks of storage, the plastics pouch tended to sag and 'breathe' a little (ICI introduced a paper sheath to keep the pouch in shape, which also provided a means of stacking the Merolite vertically in the refrigerator or on the shelf and displayed the product label). But the biggest and, in the end, insurmountable difficulty was filling the pouch and sealing it in such a way that the carbon dioxide did not escape, and in tackling this problem ICI discovered some harsh facts about the market-place.

ICI Plastics Division were not, and never had been, in the retail business. Rolls of flexible film, tanker-loads of granules, or any form of bulk chemical found them thoroughly versed in the techniques of manufacture and completely familiar with the requirements of their customers. Other ICI divisions, notably those for paints, agricultural and gardening products, and at that time the petrol retailing arm, were more familiar with the High Streets of Britain, but two factors prevented the Plastics Division from tapping this experience. In the first place, ICI had just emerged from a period of severe rationalisation; they had been, by their own admission, heavily over-staffed in the early 1960s and had now pared their middle management to the bone – there was simply no one with relevant experience who could be spared. Second, there is a world of difference between retailing paint or gardening products, on the one hand, and entering the fizzy drinks business on the other. The Plastics Division were to find themselves in exactly the same position as Dunlop were to face with their Denovo tyre – that of operating at one remove from customers in the shops, and of being forced to sell a concept, not to the retailer, but to the man in the middle – in this case the manufacturer of soft drinks or beer. What interested the manufacturer was not only the appeal Merolite might have to his eventual customers, but also the mechanics – and hence the economics – of filling the container, and this is where the ICI research team really found themselves straying out of their depth.

The system they devised for putting the drinks into their Merolite pouches and then sealing them in was in itself highly ingenious. The pouches arrived at the filling line in cartridges, each of which contained 900 flattened containers. These were fed in turn onto the filling line, the first station of which consisted of a filling tube that was inserted into the hole at the top of the Merolite pouch, and which first filled it with carbon dioxide, then poured in the beverage. This process was then reversed for an instant, as the filling head was emptied of liquid to prepare it for the next puff of gas; the pouch meanwhile moved on to another station at which a patch of sealing tape was placed over the hole and heated to fix it firmly into position. Virtually no carbon dioxide escaped during this process, and the fizz would then stay in the pouch until the consumer stripped off the opening tape.

The problem, inevitably, was that of designing and manufacturing this unique filling equipment, and ICI found themselves pitched into a branch of industry totally unlike any they had ever tackled before, and in which they were to come totally unstuck. They tried to persuade the specialists in the field to take over the

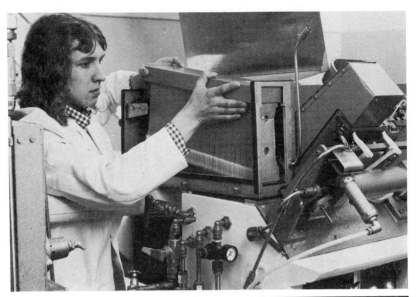

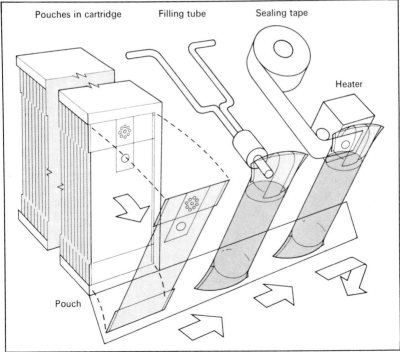

Pouches in cartridge   Filling tube   Sealing tape

Heater

Pouch

A cartridge of Merolite containers being loaded for filling (top) and (bottom) the schematic arrangement of the filling line

job, but the makers of packaging equipment simply didn't want to know. They were manufacturing canning equipment that could fill *1000* cans a minute, and bottling lines running at 300 a minute. The puff-pour-suck routine of filling a Merolite pouch could never, in their opinion, match these speeds and they were not interested in committing themselves to the expensive development work needed for a production line whose future, as they saw it, was less than rosy.

ICI bravely decided to go it alone. They believed the Merolite line could be used by relatively small factories that could not afford the huge investment needed for the very fast canning or bottling lines, and would be tempted by the thought that investment in Merolite filling equipment could be built up stage by stage. In other words, they could start by buying a single filling line and then, as demand grew, increase their production capacity simply by buying another identical unit, then another, and so on – a growth pattern that would not make sense with the other methods of packaging. In their publicity, ICI stressed the 'small-is-beautiful' line, and must have been mildly surprised that the first serious approach they had was from, of all people, the mighty Watney Mann corporation. Watney Mann – always on the look-out for new marketing ideas – were intrigued by the Merolite concept, and it is ICI's contention that the brewers actually persuaded them to gamble on an early experimental launch of beer in Merolite containers rather sooner than ICI thought wise. Whatever the truth of the matter, 1973 saw the first Merolite containers with their Watney Mann beer arriving in the shops to test the temperature of the market. As the brewers knew, and the ICI people were about to learn, they could not have chosen a more turbulent ocean.

Until 1935, glass had dominated the whole of the drinks container business, with only a few stone bottles to challenge its monopoly. The first attempt to put drinks into a can was a bottle-shaped tin with a crown top, and no one paid a great deal of attention to the newcomer. Britain's first real experience of fizzy drinks in cans resulted from Allied Breweries' decision, in the 1950s, to produce a beer specially blended to suit the metal container, and Long-Life was Britain's first mass-produced canned beer, and the start of a new era in drinks packaging. In 1965 glass still dominated the market, selling 1200 million bottles against a mere 400 million cans, but then came the supermarket boom and a completely different pattern of selling drinks. Six-packs of cans took less space on the shelf and they could be stacked one on top of another. Preoccupied as they were with the cost-effective use of space, supermarkets would not handle returnable bottles, and cans never pretended to require more than one trip. By 1970 cans and bottles were absolutely neck and neck.

Bottles still had some important advantages over cans. Until the arrival of the ring-pull can, opening and drinking from a can required a special opener, which as often as not was not in the right place at the right time, whereas screw-top bottles were not only easier to open, but could be closed on a partially empty bottle to retain the remainder of the fizz. Bottles looked more elegant, and it was possible for manufacturers to design their own identifiable shape of bottle which could be instantly recognised by the consumer; the only real difference between one can and another was the printed label. Most important of all, bottles were significantly cheaper to buy, by as much as one penny for a 10-fluid-ounce container.

But if the glass manufacturers still had these selling points in their favour, they lost their equal share of the market as the result, partially, of one disastrous miscalculation. The hot summer of 1973 produced a massive demand for carbonated drinks, and the glass people were caught napping; they had underestimated the number of drinks people would buy and were unable to manufacture the extra bottles demanded by the drink firms. In this boom year, the new capacity could only be met by cans and both the brewers and the soft-drinks manufacturers went for canning lines. By 1975 the cans had it, and it was the turn of the glass people to try and claw back their share of the business by introducing new attractions.

The first of these was a 'twist-off' top for smaller bottles; an attempt to combine the virtues of the crown top (which needed a bottle-opener before one could get at the contents) with those of a screw-top (which was that much less economical to manufacture). The problem with the twist-off was that fingers and thumbs tended to be lacerated by the sharp edges of the cap, which was fixed to the bottle too tightly for easy removal. Then, and more successfully, came the 'wide-mouth', which had an opening wide enough to make it positively comfortable to drink from a bottle, with a ring-pull similar to that of a can. Some brewers (and particularly those selling up-market products like Theakstons' Old Peculiar) took to the wide-mouth with enthusiasm, and there was a middle-class cult for recycling the empties as storage jars.

But, in the meantime, the ecological battle was also warming up. The Friends of the Earth were conducting an all-out campaign against Schweppes' progressive movement towards one-trip bottles, and were littering the fronts of supermarkets with symbolic deposits of empties. The glass manufacturers fought back with economic arguments, claiming that it was the customer who made it unrealistic to operate the sale-or-return system. Their argument ran as follows: the kind of durable bottle that was capable of standing up to a number of journeys to and from the bottlers had to be made of heavier glass than the one-trip version, and this entailed an extra cost that could only be recouped if the bottles were sold and returned an average of eight times. In Scotland the careful (not to say canny) folk actually managed an average of 15 trips per bottle, and public houses – which simply poured out the drinks at the counter and then put the bottle straight back into wooden crates – achieved as many as 19 exchanges between brewery and customer. Elsewhere, however, the careless behaviour of the consumer cost the bottler money; in London the average number of journeys was as low as three, while seaside resorts and other day-trip havens seldom got the bottles back even once. Why, said the drinks people, should we subsidise the environmentalists when we're actually burning more fuel, wasting more resources, and losing money because of the behaviour of our customers?

The argument was complicated, of course, by the fact that bottlers would only take back their own empties, which frustrated the consumer trying to return the wrong brand of bottle to an unwelcoming store, and in an ideal world perhaps all bottles would be compatible with all filling lines. The glass people, meanwhile, tried to divert attention to the fact that the canners were under no pressure at all in Britain to recycle *their* empties, although tin and aluminium were more precious resources than the sand from which glass was made. There were states in America that insisted on both bottles and cans carrying a cash deposit, but the movement did not seem to be gaining much impetus, and the whole debate was, and is, in danger of sinking beneath a sea of arguments and counter-arguments. Not surprisingly, the drinks people focused their attention on the strict economics of both methods, comparing the superior filling speeds possible on a canning line with the relative economies of installing a bottling line; three times the speed with cans, half the capital cost with bottles. It was into this cauldron of competition that ICI arrived in the early 1970s.

A thorough market survey following the Watney Mann trial indicated that the consumers liked Merolite, provided that they could be persuaded to buy it. There was, as we have seen, a distinct first-time resistance to the awkward-looking product and its difficult drinking action, but familiarity seemed to breed content, rather than contempt, and ICI were encouraged by the results of the survey. Watney Mann decided, ominously, to pull out of the experiment at this stage and to 'wait until the production process attained higher speeds', but ICI's attempts to attract small drinks firms were having some success. By 1976 they had secured nine customers and had also established their own factory in Dumfries to manufacture the plastics film. At the same time, they had taken an even more ambitious step in deciding to launch Merolite in Europe. One of the largest producers of soft drinks in Holland, NV Hero Conserven, had agreed to sell their line of 'Pitshop' drinks in Merolite pouches, and ICI backed this move by establishing a second plastics plant in Kerkrade, near the Dutch-German border. Three engineering firms were making the filling equipment to ICI's design, and the production lines were then leased to the companies that made the drinks. In effect, ICI were shouldering the bulk of the risk, and their investment had climbed to the £7 million mark. And now the storm clouds were gathering over the whole project.

It was at this point that 'The Risk Business' team approached the ICI Plastics Division with a view to involving them in a programme about Merolite. What we weren't to know was that there was a fierce internal debate among ICI management, some of whom had already decided that the project should be terminated, while others believed that time would sort out the problems. In Scotland, indeed, a positive market pull towards the new product was emerging and the Merolite users there were convinced that the future was rosy. But elsewhere the picture was grim; it was conceded by the most ardent champions of the project that filling speeds could never match those of bottles, still less those of cans, and the lack of retail experience in the Plastics Division was becoming ever more evident. Furthermore, their hopes of producing a film capable of satisfying the makers of really fizzy drinks – and these were the major drinks manufacturers – were fading rapidly. All these points became clear to us in preparing the programme, and were spelt out on the air.

The day after our transmission, we were called by at least one of Merolite's customers who had learnt for the first time of the rapidly deteriorating situation, and in the year that followed the pessimists of the Plastics Division were proved right. The plants in Scotland and Holland were closed down, and Merolite is now officially dead. Perhaps it was simply ahead of its time, or perhaps – like the Denovo tyre – it stands as a daunting example of the difficulties of launching what is fundamentally a consumer product when the innovators themselves have no direct access to the market-place. Like Dunlop, ICI tried everything they could to demonstrate the attractions of their product to the buying public, but unlike the Denovo team the Plastics Division eventually decided it had had enough. Frivolous products of this kind are an episode ICI would like to forget, and for the time being they are concentrating on the bulk chemicals and other products they know they can produce for customers they understand. Some very unfunny things can happen on the way to the High Street.

Chapter Five

On the Carpet

Mr Tufted meets the Weavers: the internecine rivalry between
the old and the new in one of Britain's least known but most
volatile industries

We had been filming with Bond Worth in their traditional weaving
sheds at Stourport when I first learnt just how cutthroat a business
carpet manufacture can be. Pleased with what we had achieved –
nobody with any feeling for Victorian engineering can fail to be
seduced by the beauty of weaving looms, the precision of the
machinery, the patience, not to say dignity, of the process
whereby row after row of carpet is painstakingly woven from rolls
of brilliantly coloured yarn – we returned to our hotel to find two
very angry executives demanding to see us. Why, they wanted to
know, had we chosen to film Bond Worth and not their firm which
was (as we well knew) bigger, better equipped, and very much in
the business of developing new machinery that could weave more
rapidly and more economically? Their arguments were reasonable, and we asked to see their new machinery. 'Not on your life,'
the two men replied; 'we don't want our rivals to know what
we're up to . . .'

It was the same when our programme went out. Why had we
chosen Edgar Pickering to represent the tufting industry? Other
companies had new technologies just as exciting and perhaps
more efficient than Edgar's newest baby, the Multicolour, which
we had featured. If we had not been aware of the fact before, we
now knew for certain that we had alighted on an industry that on
the surface seemed placid, perhaps old-fashioned, even dull, but
which when one opened the hive turned out to be swarming with
new ideas and internecine rivalry. Fortunately, we were able to
defend ourselves by sending the complainants a very handsome
tribute paid to the programme by the industry's own magazine,
Carpet Review Weekly, and the reason for recalling the
uncomfortable experience is simply to highlight the strength of
feeling and initiative that underlies the British carpet industry.

One reason the carpet industry receives very little publicity is that it has been a very healthy one for a number of years. It has not gone with its begging bowl to Westminster, pleading for government support to protect it from unfair competition from overseas. Some firms have died, but others have grown to replace them. There have been distinct shifts of balance – the tufters have certainly cut great swathes out of the weavers' share of the home market – but above all this is an industry that has prospered on overseas sales. Britain weaves carpets as well as anyone in the world, and we probably make the best tufting machinery as well. The paradox of the carpet industry today is that it is threatened – and for the first time it really *is* threatened – by its own success. Success, above all, in designing and developing new methods of making carpets.

It would be wrong to suggest that 'conversion', as it is called, is the only economically important part of the carpet-making process. It is certainly the most visible – conversion is the point at which all the raw materials come together to be woven or tufted into what is recognisably a carpet – and it has encouraged a constant succession of new designs, and even of completely new approaches to an unpromising corner of engineering. But carpet making is as vulnerable as any other industry to increases in the price of raw materials: in the winter of 1976, during which we were filming, the price of yarn alone went up by 15 per cent! Manning levels and wages also matter a great deal: one of the crucial factors in the battle between woven and tufted carpets has been the fact that it takes fewer, less skilled men to operate tufting machines than to supervise the intricate process of weaving. And the High Street obviously has its say: at the end of the day, the customer is going to choose the pattern she or he wants, and a carpet maker depends a great deal on the skill of his pattern designers. (Unfortunately, this is a business dominated by 'down-market' choice. By and large, the profitable firms are not the ones that produce sophisticated designs of the kinds featured in glossy magazines; florid, not to say lurid, patterns rule with carpets because they are what the customer – in Britain and abroad – seems to want to buy.)

But when all is said and done, 'conversion' represents the heart of the action, where competition between different companies and the skill of their engineering designers really counts, and it is to conversion that this chapter is devoted. The major division in the carpet industry is between weaving machines and tufting machines. Weaving is the tried and trusted method, with roots in the Middle Ages and with its heyday of technical innovation coinciding with the bloom of Victorian ingenuity. The jacquard, which uses perforated cards to instruct the loom to select individual colours for each stage of the weave, was perhaps 70 years ahead of its time, and its punched cards bear an uncanny resemblance to those used by today's computers.

Within weaving, one has to distinguish between two different kinds of loom, the Axminster and the Wilton; both are with us today, although many people in the industry believe that the Wilton's days are numbered. The Wilton receives its yarn from a large number of bobbins at the back of the machine. As the yarn is fed into the loom, the jacquard dictates which colours are to be lifted to the top of the weave, and which – the remaining four fifths – are to be left invisible in the backing. The shuttle then flies across, threading jute to hold the yarn in place, and the jacquard instructs another set of colours to appear on the surface while a knife crosses the completed weave, cutting the loops to leave an upstanding pile. It all needs a skilled weaver to keep an eye on every part of the machine's performance. Looms can lose their tension, individual 'ends' of yarn can be broken, any of the hundreds of intricate moving parts can run into trouble – and above all, the bobbins at the back need to be constantly replaced as they run out of yarn. The biggest expense of the Wilton process, however, lies in the fact that so much expensive yarn is wasted in the backing. Where other carpet processes use jute or hessian or latex to provide the foundation for the pattern, Wiltons bury four

Traditional carpet weaving on a Wilton loom

fifths of the yarn out of sight. It makes for a superb quality carpet, but few people these days can afford that kind of luxury.

The Axminster does not suffer in the same way. Its backing is unashamedly jute, and what happens here is that a long chain of rollers feeds the loom with a different set of colours for every row in the pattern. Each individual roll slides into position, its various ends of yarn are threaded through the jute and bound into place by the flying shuttle, then the ends are cut off and the roller moves on to make room for the next one. Again the machine needs a great deal of mechanical supervision, and master weavers take tremendous pride in their machines and the quality of their weave. For this they earn good wages – some in 1978 were reckoned to get around £120 a week, though the official figure is somewhat lower than that.

The cost of the Axminster comes from the very laborious business of loading those individually packed rollers. Once again the variously coloured yarn arrives on bobbins, but instead of the punched-card jacquard selecting the colours as they travel through the loom, the selection here is made by hand. The designer's artwork is converted into a code that denotes the different colours of every stitch in the carpet, and girls busily load the precise colours needed for each roll according to the instruction card – two girls changing the bobbins on a large frame, a third girl winding the yarn off the frame and onto the rollers which will in turn be loaded onto the loom. These girls earned over £3,000 a year on a shift pattern in 1978, and although they work fast, their jobs are by their very nature somewhat slow and unaided by modern automation. Bond Worth themselves designed a large curved frame to enable the girls to load their bobbins reasonably conveniently, but it takes a human eye and brain to match the numbers on the instruction card to the colours on the bobbin.

The result is a carpet costing around £10 a square metre – depending on the quality of the yarn – and which is a work of quality and love. Jack Meacham, the master weaver we filmed at Bond Worth, talked of the pride he felt when he walked into a hotel, say, and recognised a Bond Worth carpet that he himself might well have woven. But in 1977, two disasters struck Bond Worth. First, they were forced to close down their Wilton lines – we filmed them during their last week of operation. The cost of that buried yarn proved just too expensive for the market to bear and Fred Mountford, a skilled weaver like his father before him, was working on the gate at Bond Worth when we next visited.

Second, and more important, Bond Worth, in August of that year, were obliged to call in the receiver. Despite a last-ditch funding from the newly formed Equity Capital for Industry, the Group found itself in a situation where losses from other divisions were gradually strangling their weaving operation. Like T & A Naylor, and other established weavers before them, Bond Worth were brought sharply up against the fact that theirs was an industry in difficulties.

Some of those difficulties emanated from a stocky, energetic man called Edgar Pickering who had set up his own factory in Blackburn to manufacture tufting machines. Edgar Pickering does not make carpets, but he produces machinery that reduces the carpet-making process to its barest and simplest essentials. The technology of tufting is very like that of the candlewick bedspread: a loop of yarn is simply threaded up through the backing and down again; then (usually) the loop is cut and the pile is left standing; a latex backing then has to be glued onto the bottom, because without it the tufts would easily become loose and fall out. That is normally how you can tell a tufted carpet – by its rubber bottom (although some tufters are crafty and stick a hessian backing on their carpets).

The other way in which a customer can often spot a tufted carpet is by the regularity of its pattern. The economy of a tufted carpet is that the machine takes the yarn continuously at high speed from creels which are not changed unless they run out. Although the different creels can hold separate colours, they will appear in the carpet in a regular order; there is no way on a tufting machine of varying the sequence in which the needles feed the yarn off their bobbins into the carpet. Gone are the skilled weavers and the elaborate machinery for providing a different colour – if need be – with every stitch. A tufting machine requires only a machine minder. Where the traditional Axminster can manage only around 21 stitches a minute, or six metres of broadloom an hour, the tufting machines can make 600 stitches a minute or six metres every 60 seconds. Tufting machines, although they are more prone to breakdown than their weaving rivals, can produce 10 times the carpet at half the cost.

And there are further advantages. The weaving industry is a father-to-son business, with skills carefully nurtured over generations. For this reason the weaving mills tend to be clustered into centres such as Kidderminster and the Stour Valley, or the South Yorkshire millstreams, and so the unions are able to secure a reasonable hold on the workforce and to ensure high wages. Tufting, however, is an industry that virtually anyone can enter; in Britain the tufting companies are spread throughout the land, and in foreign countries, even with unskilled workforces, it is not hard to establish a tufted carpet industry where a weaving business would be inconceivable. There is no craft involved, and therefore no craft association; the wages remain low and the workforce flexible, if not casual. It all serves to keep prices down.

Edgar Pickering in many ways epitomises the tufting trade. He was born in Blackburn and he took his first job at the age of 14, loading sacks at a flour mill. He was paid the princely sum of seven shillings and sixpence a week and, as he says today, 'You soon decide, when you are moving 280 lbs of flour, that you're either going to be a very strong idiot, or you get the hell out of it.' He did the latter. He joined a loom company in Blackburn (Lancashire is still the centre of the textile machinery industry in Britain) and he rose to the top with astronomical speed – he was managing director at the age of 26. He stayed with the Blackburn Loom company (now defunct) until 1956, when he took the managing director's job at a new company, Cobble Brothers, set up to make tufting machinery. At this time tufting was virtually unknown in Britain. It had in fact been the discovery of a girl called Katherine Evans in Georgia, USA, who had come across the technique in the 1890s when she was only 14 years old, and the industry grew slowly in the United States without penetrating Britain, which was still very much dominated by the weavers. Cobbles, aptly enough, had been in business only a few years when they were taken over by the American giant, Singers. This was enough for Pickering, who didn't want to work for a memo-pushing corporation ('You can't run a business when you get forms coming in from Head Office demanding to know what is a man's name, what is his sex, what is the colour of his eyes and things of that nature.') In 1964, he set up shop just across the road from Cobbles, determined to make better tufting machines than his old employers, and to break the American monopoly of the tufting industry.

Edgar Pickering

Although he would not admit it, Edgar Pickering is very much a design engineer. His approach was hardly that of the high technologist: 'It was designed, literally, out of our hands. We planned it by bringing in an engineer on one side and a joiner on the other, and we made a wooden mock-up of what I wanted the machine to look like. If you looked at that wooden model today it is identical to the super-duper glossy machines coming off our factory floor.' So says Edgar. He knew what he wanted, and he knew exactly how to go about it. Even today he is capable of spotting a machine in difficulties and of diagnosing and curing the ailment as fast as any of his technicians, and back in the early 1960s he knew just what was needed to refine the fairly basic tufting machines then being made. His design introduced a variable bedplate so that the height of stitches could be altered according to the depth of carpet the maker wanted to produce. He introduced a choice of needlebars so that the number of stitches per inch could also be altered with only a minor adjustment. He also provided a variable-speed motor to control the amount of yarn being fed into the carpet – three means of providing different qualities of tuft, ranging from a loose, cheap tuft at the bottom end to a precise, tightly tufted carpet at the top that rivalled the best of Wiltons, but which cost only a fraction of the price. As the weavers themselves admit, it does not make much difference to the quality whether you weave or tuft a carpet, it's what you put into the product that counts, and Edgar's machines made it possible for the aspiring tufter to produce carpets as good as any weaver – except, of course, that he couldn't produce a patterned pile.

Setting up on his own was by no means easy. Raising the finance was, as ever in Britain, a nightmare (and at least one major manufacturer of textile machinery today rues the day he turned away Edgar Pickering when he came to ask for help). He set up with £10,000 of his own money and £10,000 from the bank – barely enough to pay the seven men who then worked for him – and for two years it was touch and go. Getting the parts he needed proved even more difficult. British suppliers were apparently scared of offending Singers and were mysteriously unable to provide Pickering with the parts he needed. He proved that he could survive without their help by buying the parts – at great expense – from overseas. The boycott ended fairly rapidly. Perhaps bitten by this experience with British suppliers, Pickerings today make virtually all their components for themselves – only the most intricate of the electronics and the largest of metal castings come from outside the plant. Everything else is tooled right there in Blackburn; around 500 people work there and virtually every machine is custom designed. Unsung design skills make it possible for the individual needs of customers to be serviced by different combinations of the various components; a certain amount of ingenuity at the drawing board means that fitters find themselves assembling a whole range of different products around, admittedly, a standard basic process. Some of Pickerings' more successful sales have come from tufting machines that can produce a variable pile height; 'contoured' carpets go down well in Germany apparently, and Pickerings have produced an electronic control not unlike a pianola roll that can change the height of the tufts as the machine churns out the carpet. It's a bolt-on extra costing around £60,000 which helps to give tufted carpets a touch of class.

And that extra hint of quality proved to be very important to the new industry. Cyril Lord was a highly successful publicist of tufted carpets in the late 1960s, but in fact he came close to branding them for ever as cheap and nasty. His use of viscose rayons gave the product a poor name, and Cyril Lord went ignominiously out of business. Pickering and the other tufters survived that crisis by introducing better artificial fibres. By 1971 the tufters were producing up to 70 million square metres a year in Britain alone, double the output of the weavers, and they had virtually cornered the lower end of the market. This coincided with a housing boom: new houses meant new carpets and, what was better still, people were using their new prosperity to carpet rooms where there hadn't been carpets before. As Edgar says, 'People used to put linoleum in the back bedrooms and just had a 40-foot square in the sitting room, or the parlour as we call it in this area. Now we want to get everybody on an image of wall-to-wall; it's got to be wall-to-wall in the bedroom, and in the kitchen as well.' And on a booming market, Pickering prospered. Not only did sales go well in Britain, but he won four Queen's Awards for Export; 85 per cent of Edgar Pickering's output goes overseas. His fitters travel from Blackburn to Manchester's Ringway Airport, and from there to every country on the map, to install his machines and to train the new operators and maintenance men.

But then came 1973, the housing boom ceased abruptly, and with it the continuing rise in the purchase of carpets. By now Pickering and his rivals had pretty well saturated the British market and – partly because his machines are very sturdily constructed – replacement sales were negligible. The only way for Pickering and the other tufters to keep their sales up was for them to make further inroads into the share of the carpet market still occupied by the weavers, and this meant moving up-market into patterned carpets.

Tufting would not be as economical as it is if the ends were reloaded to make way for fresh colours in the middle of their weave. To use an analogy with knitting, when tufting you can't change the balls of wool once you've started, and you are committed to using the colours you've got in a regular sequence. One way of producing a varied pattern is to tuft a plain white carpet and then dye the pattern onto the pile. Dyed or printed tufted carpets are now fairly common, but their critics point out that they lack the precision of pattern that an Axminster or Wilton can supply (every individual stitch in these woven carpets can be different from the ones around it) and furthermore, dyed wool suffers from the same problem as dyed hair – the colour rarely reaches down to the base, and with wear the roots sometimes begin to show! Edgar Pickering reckoned there had to be a better way to challenge the weavers, and once again he found his inspiration on the other side of the Atlantic.

The Crawford Pickering Multicolour is a giant machine of which Heath Robinson would have been very proud. Designed by an American inventor, Crawford, it is designed to get round that problem of knitting from unalterable balls of wool by the not entirely simple device of using a multicoloured ball of wool. If you can't change the yarn as it is fed into the tufting machine, then change the colour of the yarn as it goes in! To describe the

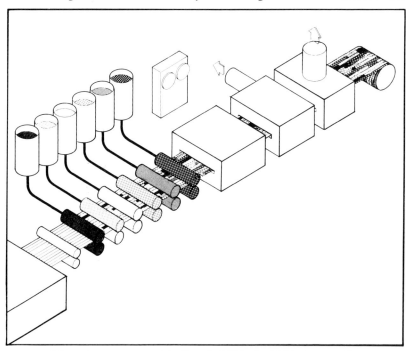

Schematic arrangement of the Crawford Pickering Multicolour machine

multicolour machine without recourse to moving pictures would, I believe, tax the verbal powers of any writer. As the yarn is fed off the creel at the start of its journey it is pure white. It then passes through 10 pairs of rollers, above each of which is a tank of dye of a different colour. The dye is fed to tiny pads on the rollers – 6000 on each roller, each of them just an inch square – whose job it is to dye the yarn as it passes through the rollers. Obviously though, the yarn must not be dyed by all the rollers, or it would end up not multicoloured, but omni-coloured – a uniform splodge of mixed dye. Part of the ingenuity of the Crawford Pickering machine is the way in which the different heads are presented to the yarn when, and only when, it is required that one section of yarn should be dyed in a particular colour. A cam behind each line of pads takes its instructions from a control bar, and if the designer wants the yarn passing through, say, the green roller to be dyed green, the cam forces the tiny pads up to make contact with the yarn. When the correct length of yarn has duly been dyed, the cam is released and the head returns to its neutral position, allowing the next section of yarn to pass by and be dyed by another roller.

So it is with each of the 10 sets of rollers, and with each of the different ends of yarn. As they all pass through the first roller, some are dyed and some are not; likewise through the second, and the third and so on. Looking down from above the rollers one can see the ends of yarn become patchy and multicoloured, a length of yellow here, another of green after it, then a stretch of blue, back to the yellow, then a brown, and so on. Of course, the trick is to make sure that the correct colour appears in the right place in the carpet when the ends come to be woven on the tufting machine, and here is where both the complexity and the problems of the Crawford Pickering design are bound to lie. After steaming the dyed yarn, to fix the colours, the system then washes and dries the ends – at which point the yarn is shrunk – and then the ends are loaded onto beams ready to be transported to the tufting machine and loaded up. The control system has to allow for the amount of shrinkage, and also for the amount of yarn that is tufted behind the backing. If the calculations have been correct, and if the various ends have been kept strictly in register with one another, the different colours will appear, almost miraculously, in the precise point of the pattern where the designer intended, and at a much faster rate than weaving looms can achieve.

As a design concept the Crawford Pickering Multicolour was breathtaking: a huge, steaming monster of a machine with so many moving parts that breakdowns seemed inevitable. Development costs rose well above the original estimates; Edgar admitted to us that the project had cost him somewhere in the region of £8 million, which is an enormous investment for a company with only 500 employees! Nonetheless, when we filmed him in September 1976 he was brimming with confidence. A calculated risk, he said, but he wasn't worried. 'The risks are over, without doubt', he said, 'and when we get the new machines into operation next year, then the market will continue to grow and grow.'

As he spoke, things had been getting more difficult still for the carpet makers. The output of tufted carpets had soared to 125 million square metres (almost twice what it had been in 1971, and almost three times the amount of woven carpet produced in Britain that year). The market, however, had not expanded at the same rate, and the retailers were beginning to get the upper hand. Because the tufters were over-producing they laid themselves open to a price-cutting war: the manufacturers saw their return on investment fall from around 20 per cent in the 1960s to a meagre eight per cent in the mid-1970s. It was not a situation in which carpet manufacturers were likely to invest in new machinery, and particularly in massively expensive and untried equipment such as the Multicolour. Through 1977, the production problems surrounding Edgar's big baby grew and grew. His multicoloured carpets were not anywhere near as precisely woven as the Axminsters he was hoping to threaten, and he had endless engineering problems. Edgar, that June, was rueful. 'We didn't take enough care in our basic engineering', he admitted. 'When we first made the decision, I don't think we realised it was going to cost as much as it has done.' That said, Edgar showed few signs of regretting his involvement in a venture at which many larger organisations would have quailed: 'Business is risk', he insisted, and when we suggested that he might have put the Multicolour on the market too soon (he was having all sorts of trouble with his customers) he was unrepentant. 'Supposing we had gone back and told the Wright Brothers not to bother to fly until we had developed the Boeing 727; would that have been developed? Would there have been this massive aircraft industry? I get tired of my engineers coming to me and saying, "If we wait until we've perfected this and we bring model number five out . . .".' As a flag-carrier for British initiative and engineering enterprise, Edgar Pickering is a noble figure. He was confident when we met that there was nothing in the Multicolour that a bit more work and a new computer control would not sort out. And if it does turn out to be another success in the brief but spectacular history of Edgar Pickering Ltd, then it will have earned a tidy sum in foreign currency. That's where he and those like him do so much for Britain – in the export market.

It's the same with the weavers. Despite Bond Worth's desperate

Dyed yarns coming off the Multicolour machine

year, Britain continues to support a healthy carpet weaving industry and to export quality products all over the world – rustic scenes woven into stair carpets for the Far East, traditional patterns for the top of the American market. There are technical innovators in the weaving industry as well as in tufting, and if they are secretive about their own developments, that could well be because they are content to produce their results, and their profits, without resort to the public purse and the glare of the media. As I said at the beginning of this chapter, the carpet industry represents an unexpected and gratifyingly enterprising corner of British industry. Long may it remain so.

Chapter Six

Not Invented Here

The struggle of a lone outsider to persuade the established
experts of Pilkington Brothers that he had indeed made the
discovery that had eluded them for half a century

'Only one designer in ten knows about Glass Reinforced Cement',
said the man in charge of the project, Lionel Blackman, 'and
that augurs for a secure future. The market can only expand.'

'The British have forgotten the meaning of the word "entrepreneur",' said Sir Alistair Pilkington, warming to his theme; 'We
give all the status to the professional or the pure scientist and
ignore the engineer and the applied scientist, despite the fact that
these are the people who actually create wealth. Why, I heard
someone last week talking about a property speculator as an
entrepreneur. People who buy and sell land don't do anything for
the nation, but innovators do, inventors do; they are the real
entrepreneurs.'

Sir Alistair has a right to his views. He not only heads a
company with a fine record for innovation (and its involvement in
Glass Reinforced Cement is just one of many new high-technology
projects it is currently developing), but Sir Alistair was himself
the entrepreneur who invented the famous 'float' method of
producing plate glass on a bed of molten tin – quality glass
manufactured without grinding or polishing, at a fraction of the
cost of the old method. One of the notable aspects of the float
glass story is the fact that Pilkington Brothers Limited had been
producing it for several months before their rivals even cottoned
on to the fact that a new method had been discovered. Another
is the fact that Alistair Pilkington was himself a relative outsider,
attending only his second manufacturing conference (in January
1952) when he proposed the molten tin method. It's true that he
was a member of the famous family that controls the company –
but he was far from being in its mainstream; his branch of the
family had broken away fully 15 generations before, and his
position in the company was by no means that of a secure family

director. When the molten tin method was going through its inevitable and serious development setbacks, the young Alistair Pilkington was well aware what was at stake should he fail.

But if the float glass story illustrates that Pilkington are a firm occasionally open to suggestions from outsiders, the story of Glass Reinforced Cement illustrates a very different and all too common situation: that of a scientist working outside the glass industry who found it very difficult indeed to persuade even Pilkington that he was capable of the breakthrough he eventually achieved, and who profited not at all from a product that can hugely benefit architects and designers and is already securing healthy returns for the companies involved in its manufacture.

Glass Reinforced Cement is exactly what the name suggests, cement (strong in compression, weak in tension) reinforced, not by iron rods, as commonly used in load-bearing structures, but by tiny fibres of glass. Usually these fibres are chopped into short lengths and sprayed simultaneously with a cement slurry into moulds, or – on site – poured or sprayed directly onto the building. The tiny glass strands hold the cement together without making it rigid, and this makes it possible to produce shapes previously thought impossible – sharp bends, slender tapered panels, very thin ducts, decorative screens and the like. Cement

Glass Reinforced Cement slurry being sprayed onto a former

can now be moulded round corners, cast with holes through it, used – in the hands of a good designer – to create really delicate effects, where before it had been considered the clodhopper, the brute of constructional materials.

The final development work on glass fibres took place at Pilkington's Research and Development Headquarters, a shining glass-fronted (as you would expect) building in the Lancashire countryside at Lathom not far from the firm's head office in St Helens. Lathom houses most of the Pilkington research work, spending around £7 million a year, or approximately two per cent of the company's turnover. Without doubt it sets the pace for Britain's glass industry, and it rivals the American giant Owens Corning in important developments in glass technology.

It was back in 1966 that a retiring, unworldly-looking scientist arrived to inform Pilkington's scientists that he believed he could crack the problem on which Lathom, and the rest of the glass industry, had been working for half a century – how to mix glass with cement. Dr Majumdar was, and still is, a government scientist working at the Building Research Establishment at Garston in Hertfordshire. To the polite surprise of the Pilkington men he turned out not to be a glass scientist at all, but a cement man whose work had brought him into contact with the reason why glass fibres had never been used to reinforce cement in the same way as they had been employed for some time, and to great effect, to reinforce plastics. The reason is simple and dramatic: cement is strongly alkaline and glass is instantly eroded by any contact with alkali. As Lionel Blackman puts it, 'Nature had ordained them enemies.'

What Dr Majumdar had done was to search through the scientific literature on the subject, and he had come across an article written in 1926 that reported that glass containing a high proportion of zirconia could stand up to the onslaught of alkali better than other kinds of glass. Majumdar also observed that most of the work on alkali-resistant glass being carried out at that time was testing E and A type glasses (the types used in glass-reinforced plastics) and that these types were not high in zirconia. To Majumdar the answer was simple: find a glass high in zirconia and use that.

Majumdar had, as he would admit himself, a lot to learn about glass. The most important factor in the manufacture of glass is to prevent any damage to the surface of the strands, because the tiniest scratch can reduce the strength of the fibres by factors of 10 or more. The exact figures are these: a skilled operator in a glass factory can 'fly-catch' a strand of fibre – he skilfully traps the end with a piece of sticky tape as it pours out of the bushing – and if he has kept that fibre from contact with any surface then it will have a tensile strength of 500,000 pounds per square inch. If, on the other hand, the fibre has come into contact with any hard object and has been nicked ever so microscopically, the strength drops to a mere 50,000 pounds per square inch. Pilkington reckon they can mass-produce glass filaments with an average strength of 250,000 pounds per square inch, and they do this by coating every single one (and there are about 200 filaments in a typical strand of glass fibre) with emulsion as it comes out of the furnace. Dr Blackman describes glass fibre production as 'organic chemistry rather than inorganic glass technology' – it's the art of coating.

The basic problem with Majumdar's theory of high-zirconia glass was that glass of this kind is highly refractory, which made it almost impossible to handle and therefore to manufacture. The Pilkington scientists listened politely to Majumdar's views and then suggested that he should come back when he had got a little further with his experiments.

Majumdar was not put off by this rejection, nor by the similar treatment he was to receive at the hands of other glass makers, including the Corning company in America. As Sir Alistair today ruefully comments, he had one key factor on his side – ignorance. Blackman puts it slightly differently: Majumdar, he says, was about to come up with a classic piece of lateral thinking. If he couldn't work from his theory to a practical solution, why not reverse the process and search for the most alkaline environment in which glass is used and then see what kind of glass has been developed to cope with these circumstances? This, he correctly surmised, might give him a glass that was both workable and would contain zirconia.

Again, the answer lay in the literature. Majumdar found a reference to 'G20', a glass used in the boilers of steam-driven power-generating stations. The environment inside such boilers is highly alkaline, and Corning had developed a special form of sight glass to make it possible to inspect the boilers visually. This was G20 and, although the sight glasses had to be replaced every few months because even this glass suffered from alkaline corrosion, Majumdar tried strenuously to get hold of a sample, certain that this would supply him with the answer he was seeking. He persuaded Corning to let him have a hundredweight of G20 cullet, but it was four months before the precious sackful arrived (finally winkled out by a Pilkington man who offered, during a visit to America, to hasten the consignment on its way just when it seemed to be blocked, or forgotten, by Corning).

Now the name of Pilkington fades out of the story for a while; it might have been for ever. The role they might have played was taken by the National Research and Development Corporation, which did not have the best of reputations among government scientists at that time, but to which all discoveries had to be referred if they were made in publicly funded laboratories, such as the Building Research Establishment. The NRDC's poor standing was based on projects it had delayed or rejected, rather than those that had got through, but in Majumdar's case the part they played was positive, not to say inspired. At the very time when industry seemed to have rejected his ideas, the NRDC gave him the necessary backing to continue with his work and when – to his intense delight – he succeeded in drawing his first strand of G20 in his Garston laboratory, the NRDC gave him enough money to commission work on a scale nearer to commercial production.

The company to which he went for help was a small one, Deeglass Fibres Ltd, although it happened that it was in the process of being taken over by Pilkington's great British rival, Turner and Co (Glasgow) Ltd. The technologists at Deeglass carried out Majumdar's instructions and succeeded in converting a substantial quantity of G20 cullet into filaments, and in coating the filaments in resin. They were doing what everyone in the industry had thought was impossible - working with high zirconia glass on an industrial scale. Majumdar hurried back to his Hertfordshire laboratories to conduct a series of further experiments, making test boards of fibres mixed with cement to see how long the glass lasted in the environment everyone had declared was too hostile for its survival.

Then, in June 1968, events began to move with lightning speed. The news of what had taken place in the workshops at Deeglass spread throughout the industry, and soon reached the office of Dr Lawrence Pilkington, the then Technical Director of the company. He realised how important it was to secure the rights, but soon came to appreciate that it was not now going to be all that simple. The NRDC, by dint of its monopoly over any work carried out by scientists working under contract to the government, had an automatic right to the overall Majumdar patent covering 'glass fibres capable of retaining their strength in a cement matrix', and of composites made from these fibres – that is, Alkali Resistant Glass, as it came to be known in the trade. But a great deal of work remained before Majumdar's G20 could be turned into fibres commercially, and the NRDC was in no position to carry out, or even to commission, the kind of work needed to bring ARG closer to manufacture. Pilkington, on the other hand, were what is more they were able to offer the NRDC their unequalled (in Britain) research and development facilities at Lathom. In return, Pilkington demanded the sole rights to supply the glass when they had developed it. In other words, any future customer of their glass would have to pay licence fees to two bodies – to the

NRDC for using the material at all, and to Pilkington because they would hold the rights over the best glass for the job. That, at any rate, was the proposal Pilkington put to the NRDC; they were trying to persuade the government body that there was no mileage for the company in pursuing expensive development work unless, at the end of the day, it secured sole rights over its own particular discovery. The NRDC, in its turn, soon realised that if Pilkington didn't do the work there was no other company in Britain capable of taking it on and the Majumdar discovery would go overseas. That, it decided, was not what the NRDC was there for, so it broke its own 'fair shares for all' rules and turned its back on Turners and the other companies who were by now anxious to secure their share of the ARG action.

In 1969, Dr Majumdar happily joined forces with the Pilkington scientists who, three years before, had turned their backs on him. Tests began on a major scale, and at break-neck speed. Before long they were making tonnes of G20 fibre for the Building Research Establishment to turn into prototype Glass Reinforced Cement products. In 1971 they developed a composition that still fitted inside their patent but which was actually not quite identical to Majumdar's original G20. This was Cem-FIL, the name under which Pilkington now make and market Alkali Resistant Glass Fibre, and a pilot plant was urgently established at Lathom to test the product under conditions of mass manufacture. Later they moved production to Wrexham, where the Group had for years been producing their conventional E type fibre. For Cem-FIL they had to develop and build a special furnace capable of heating the new mixture to temperatures above 1500°C, then bleed off any of the molten glass that had become contaminated by contact with the surface of the furnace. They will increase production to many thousand tonnes by 1980 because, as Blackman says, they believe that the market is going to grow and grow.

But the complications had by no means finished yet. The first and most immediate problem facing the Pilkington team was that of controlling the use of Cem-FIL in an industry – the construction business – notorious for taking short-cuts and trimming safety margins. The experience of seeing the vinyl industry shot down in flames by a holocaust in the vinyl-clad leisure centre in the Isle of Man was enough to remind them that one disaster can give the whole of a product range a bad name, wherever the true fault lies.

Pilkington came up with a novel, and controversial, solution to the problem of uncontrolled secondary use of GRC. It had previously been the intention of the Cem-FIL team merely to develop a market for Glass Reinforced Cement and then to sell Cem-FIL to anyone interested – the normal way of doing business. However, when news started filtering back to Pilkington of shoddy, not to say dangerous, products being constructed from their new product, the company quickly decided that they could not afford to lose control over the uses to which Cem-FIL was to be put and they decided that the best way to exercise that control was to introduce a form of licensing. Now they still sell Cem-FIL fibre, but they also license the use of it, and only issue these licences to concerns who have demonstrated that they will practise a high degree of quality control and thus are not likely to give the product a bad name by careless application.

There were inevitably rumblings of monopoly restrictions and of excessive pricing. It is not for the outsider to judge whether Pilkington acted purely out of concern for the good name of Cem-FIL, or whether there was some element of commercial awareness that they had such a unique product that they could, in effect, name their own terms. Their patent is certainly secure; other manufacturers are in theory able (under licence from the NRDC) to develop their own compositions for Alkali Resistant Glass, but Pilkington believe they have carved themselves out the most valuable slice of the chemical spectrum and that nobody working outside their boundaries stands much chance of coming out with a workable ARG. The early years have been spent not only in learning how better to manufacture Cem-FIL but also in discovering how to *use* it. A small team at Pilkington has been headed by a design engineer fresh from working on the concrete containment vessels for nuclear power stations; his designers have drawn up the basic specifications for the new cement and taught the licensees how to apply them. One example of their work comes from ARC, a construction company 'big in drains'. Here they wrap the glass fibre continuously (it is normally chopped up into short strands) inside a spinning steel mould, then they form a core of conventional concrete within this layer, and then finally they wrap another layer of the GRC on the inside to complete a concrete sandwich. This, they found, produced pipes capable of equalling the performance of conventional pipes weighing twice as much, and furthermore they could avoid the awkward 'bell' mouth which characterises all other pipes. This in turn was a joy to the men digging the holes for the pipes, who no longer had to dig a deep trench wherever the pipes joined, just to accommodate the bell.

But any product as revolutionary as Glass Reinforced Cement is going to take time before it satisfies everybody that there are no dangers involved. GRC is still not used for permanent load-bearing applications because, says Blackman, 'It is mere common sense to want many, many years of working experience with the new material before being prepared to take any significant risk, where failure would hazard life and limb.' In fact, the nagging fear remains that the glass may not be permanently resistant to the alkali in cement, especially if the conditions under which it is used – wet, dry, hot, etc – should happen to have an unpredicted effect on the glass-cement mix. If the glass should be eaten away by the alkali in time, what would be the strength of the no longer reinforced cement? Both Pilkington and the Department of the Environment conducted exhaustive assessment of the problem and both were satisfied. Currently, however, the use of GRC is confined to cladding and such peripheral areas as ducting, piping

Laying uniform section ARC glass reinforced drain pipes

and garden furniture. Work continues on more advanced glasses and Blackman reckons that before the turn of the century there may well be major developments, but in the meantime, as he says, 'We're all being very cautious . . .'

There are other problems that Pilkington have successfully laid to rest. When the vinyl-based plastics fascia of the Isle of Man leisure centre erupted into flames, the whole of the plastics industry was severely burnt in the backlash; architects were nervous of using plastics in any kind of frontage and local authorities became twice as careful in permitting new materials to be used in buildings. Thus, before the Greater London Council would give permission for GRC to be used in the NatWest Tower in the City of London, it insisted on intensive one-hour tests against British Standards, with no higher than a two per cent failure rate. The Pilkington team obliged with 50 separate tests during which only one panel failed and, exhausted with the continuous effort, they turned to the inspectors for approval. Nothing doing, said the men from the GLC; two per cent means two out of a 100, and we want 100 separate tests. Nervously, Blackman's men set about a further 50 tests, producing this time only one 'partial' failure. As a result, the NatWest Tower has service ducting built from GRC; the alternative material to follow the awkward angles of their giant company logo (how many passers-by appreciate that the tower is built in the shape of the bank's emblem?) would have been steel, and steel is many times more expensive than cement. Conventional cement could

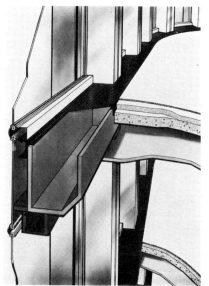

GRC heating ducts are cheaper than steel for difficult shapes

The Crédit Lyonnais building (top) uses Cem-FIL cladding and the giant NatWest Tower has service ducting made from GRC

never have been moulded precisely enough for this job, nor could it have been envisaged for Cem-FIL's most notable early edifice, the Crédit Lyonnais building, also in the City of London. Jeremy Mackay Lewis was the architect of this bank, curiously petite beside the monoliths of the Golden Mile, which features delicately tapered arches in its cladding, and he used the design possibilities of GRC to their full. What is important, therefore, is that the material can now be used for almost any category of building, even in tower blocks where the hazard of fire is felt most keenly.

This chapter started with an indication of the future potential of GRC. Even setting aside any thought at present of using it for load-bearing structures, there are many, many applications for which designers of the next decade will be grateful that they can use low-cost cement, rather than steel or other more expensive alternatives. But Pilkington – whom I acknowledge to be one of the most enterprising of British companies – can't duck the fact that the GRC story shows how easily the most sophisticated, most enlightened in-house team can suffer from tunnel vision, especially when the problem in question has been knocking around their laboratories for years. However unimpressive the outsider may seem, can a company ever afford to say no to an idea simply because it was Not Invented Here?

But the fault does not lie solely with the big research and development team, fashionable though it is to shoot at sizeable targets. Britain tends to flatter its individual designers and inventors into believing that the world owes them a living – that their genius is an automatic bread-ticket to the production line, to the High Street, to fame and fortune. It isn't, of course, which brings us back to Sir Alistair's plea for the return of the entrepreneur to the laboratories and development groups of Britain. Dr Majumdar is, by all accounts, happy to be back in his government laboratory without having earned a red cent from his discovery of alkali-resistant glass. A huge gap apparently exists between the supposedly harsh world of industry and the supposedly cosy corridors of the university and the research institutes. In Britain, that is.

Chapter Seven

No More Than Twenty

Innovation by design: the startling results of the decision
by Glynwed, a traditionally based engineering group, to set up
a unique troubleshooting research team with only
a score of members

The foundry at historic Coalbrookdale is typical of the problems facing this struggling sector of British industry. The equipment the foundrymen use looks for all the world as though it had been installed back in 1709, when Abraham Darby first succeeded in smelting iron with coke. Above the workers' heads, the ceilings let in daylight and rain between dilapidated corrugated panels. Dust fills the gloomy air, and the tripper on his way to the Ironbridge Museum and the old furnace site next door to the foundry might be forgiven for thinking that the only new investment this century has been in the smart new sign proclaiming the name of the present owners, Glynwed.

There is, however, one major innovation inside the Coalbrookdale foundry, and it has happened here because Glynwed decided in 1976 to employ a remarkable entrepreneur and to allow him to establish a design and research hot-house with the job of taking a long, hard look at the Glynwed operations and to rationalise, improve, and if necessary radically to redesign either the production process or the product itself. This chapter tells the story of Dr Ron Clark and his Central Resources Unit, which is unique of its kind in Britain.

Establishing the CRU was not an act that seems at all characteristic of Glynwed, a conservative engineering consortium based in the Midlands. Their headquarters at Sheldon, near Birmingham, positively exude prosperity, but it is wealth based on a very traditional variety of products made by a wide range of member companies: bathroom fittings by Leisure, Rayburn heaters and Aga cookers all come under the Glynwed umbrella, as well as screws, bearings, tubes and fastenings, with a wholesale chemicals company on top of that. Then there are window frame manufacturers, steelworks and, of course, foundries.

Glynwed must have been tempted to write off their foundry operation as a lost cause, in common with many other owners of foundries throughout Britain. In fact, the experiment Ron Clark is conducting at Coalbrookdale probably represents the first major innovation in iron casting this century, in that it makes it possible to turn out fine castings of the sort that had previously to be crafted by hand, by methods as simple as those which in the past have been reserved for relatively crude mass production of cheaper products.

The method generally used to cast, say, a cooker hob cover is very close to the one that Abraham Darby devised. The pattern for the hob cover is placed in the lower half of a moulding box and a mixture of sand and clay is rammed around it so tightly that it will not be displaced when the pattern is removed. The lower half of the box is then turned over and 'parting powder' is poured over it – this contains an additive such as coal dust that will 'flash' at the moment when molten metal is poured into the mould and will ensure a smooth surface on the iron as it is cast. The upper half of the moulding box is then placed on top of the lower, a wedge is placed immediately above the mould, and the top half in turn is filled with the 'green sand' mixture which is compacted into shape around the pattern. When the sand is firm, the two halves are split and the pattern is removed; then the box is put together again with an empty hole inside it in the exact shape of the pattern. The wedge is then removed, leaving a channel through which the molten metal can be poured into the hole. In goes the molten metal, and the filled mould is left to cool. Eventually the box is split to reveal an iron casting in the shape of the original pattern. The runner (the iron that has solidified in the hole left by the wedge) is broken off with a hammer, and the casting is taken for finishing to a grinding shop. So far so good for relatively simple shapes, but intricate cast iron has to be 'fettled' largely by hand and this in turn means that every job is virtually

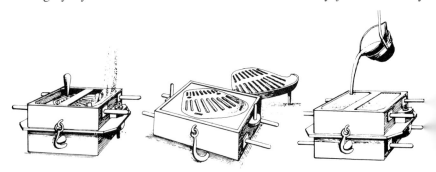

The traditional casting process used to produce a fire grate

a one-off and extremely expensive. That's where the CRU's vacuum moulding technique comes in.

Put simply, vacuum moulding holds the sand in place by sucking out all the air in the moulding box; this additional firmness makes it possible to mould the sand around much more intricate patterns than with the traditional green sand method.

The Glynwed CRU vacuum casting technique – the polythene sheet 'flashing' is visible on the moulding box

Second, instead of parting powder, the 'flashing' is performed in this process by a polythene sheet stretched over the hole left by the pattern and sucked into the curves and nooks of the design by the same suction process that compacts the sand. The Japanese – who devised vacuum moulding – don't understand precisely how this flashing works, but what the CRU are learning at Coalbrookdale is that it certainly achieves the desired result.

And they are not leaving it at that. In association with metallurgists at Oxford University, Glynwed's Central Resources Unit are researching and analysing the vacuum moulding process. They reckon they are learning more about it than the Japanese from whom they have licensed it. Their knowledge could, they believe, give Glynwed a world lead in this new field of producing fine castings in the sort of volume previously only possible with relatively simple patterns. The workforce at the Coalbrookdale foundry are said to be walking with their heads a little higher; they believe that their leaky roof actually houses one of the most significant innovations that foundries are likely to witness in a very long time.

Vacuum casting is one example; and to it must be added a whole list of pioneering projects undertaken by the Glynwed research team: a rippled airbed for long-stay hospital patients; a family of gas, smoke and burglar detectors; a shower that can recycle its own water; the use of nitrogen to save fuel in steel furnaces; a vandal-proof dial for telephone kiosks; silent heat convectors; a completely new range of plastic windows; infra-red

The 20-strong CRU team led by Dr Ron Clark

cookers; heat exchangers for domestic use; an ultra-simple window lock . . . It sounds a lot like the short-list in a national design competition; in fact it represents the work achieved over two years by 20 people, working under one rather unusual man.

Dr Ron Clark (everyone seems to call him Doctor; he's very proud of the title) is 57 years old and at first sight the very image of a self-made businessman of the sort you'd expect to run his own plumbing business or a chain of hardware stores. It might, indeed, have turned out that way but for the war, when Clark found his way into the army, serving in the Far East and from there, as a prisoner of war, on to the Siam-Burma Railway of *Bridge over the River Kwai* fame. It was in hospital recovering from that experience that the then 28-year-old cockney 'discovered' education . . . and it gripped him like a vice. With 600 others he applied for a place on a teacher training course at Leeds University, and Clark was one of the 90 selected. He also seems to have caught the eye of course director Alistair Maclennan, because the three years at Leeds turned the apprentice plumber's mate from being just a wide-eyed novice in the world of learning into a combination of first-rate technologist and teacher, and it is to 'Mac's' personal guidance that Clark today attributes this very rapid graduation.

For the rest of his career, Clark has moved between teaching jobs in technical colleges and universities, with occasional sorties into industry. Somewhere along the way he picked up a doctorate in noise and vibration at Southampton University – hence the title – and his last job before Glynwed was on the board of a West Country manufacturing firm. Here he found himself in severe disagreement with a take-over policy, and – typical of the man, perhaps – resigned on the spot. After this, he found himself face to face with another board, that of Glynwed, putting to them what must have seemed an extraordinary proposition: he would take the job they were offering him – that of technical director – if they would let him try a unique experiment in research and development.

Glynwed, like all other engineering firms, were feeling the pinch of increased fuel costs, high-technology competition from overseas, and antiquated and therefore very expensive production machinery. They must have been conscious also that many of their product ranges were in need of fresh ideas.

What Clark was proposing was the establishment of a research and development 'profit centre'. He was not in fact asking for a great deal of money, either then or later; 'Give me', he said, '£280,000 for the first year and I shall prove to you that my research and design can save the Group money.'

It is a tribute to Clark's persuasive powers that the Board was willing to 'give it a go', and he set up shop in a small, low-cost and unpretentious factory unit a couple of miles away from Headland House, the Group's headquarters.

Clark set a figure of 20 for his team – no more, no less – because that was the number he felt could work together and yet achieve the variety of projects that would attract the very best talents. As his lieutenant he brought with him from the West Country Tony Hayward, many years his junior, but who runs the CRU as Manager of Research and Development. The next move was to bring in a small, hard-core team of professional managers for specific roles within the Unit. Clark did not want to develop a precious hot-house environment in which projects were started for technology's sake without a real hope of selling in the market-place, so he brought in Phil Sidell as Marketing Manager to conduct thorough surveys of the sales prospects of every CRU project. Remarkably for a team of so few people, he hired a resident designer, Mike Rodger; Clark and Hayward put a very high premium on the appearance and presentation even of their prototypes. So their designs would look good, and they could reassure their 'clients' – the various divisions of Glynwed – that a market existed, but Clark knew from experience that the most common response from the hardened production director who faces a bright-eyed whizz-kid from outside is to say 'Nice idea, old son, but you simply don't understand *my* problems.' Well, they anticipated that one too, and brought in Malcolm Childs as their first Production Director, with the job of ensuring that any CRU product was properly designed and realistically costed for production in the 'real' world.

That was the kernel around which the CRU was built, and the financial context was both simple in concept and complex in reality. The Unit's budget was meant to cover all the costs entailed inside the four walls of the research and development building, while the divisions of Glynwed, if they liked the idea, would meet all further costs. Clark presents himself annually to the Board and gives an account of his stewardship, confident that he will be able to argue that the money has been more than recouped by the service the Unit has supplied. He then outlines the projects they have on the drawing board for next year – carefully costed – and persuades the Board to put up the necessary budget, hoping that the following year he will be able to come back again and account for it in the same way.

In fact, life has not proved to be quite so simple. Even on as clear a project as energy-saving in the steel furnaces, Clark ran up against resistance from line directors who were unwilling to dip into their own pockets for the money necessary to implement his ideas.

The CRU had been asked by the Group's Chairman to 'look into energy' in the furnaces. Research indicated that a lot of precious fuel could be saved if the furnaces were switched from endothermic gases to use nitrogen instead, but when Clark presented this suggestion to the management of Darleston – one of the most old-fashioned mills in the Group – he found no immediate willingness to spend the money required for the conversion. In fact, to persuade them to give him their very oldest furnace to play with, and £5000 of the division's money to help meet the costs, he had to dip into the Unit's own budget for a further £5000 before the alterations could be carried out. The experiment worked, and the Steel Division agreed to convert their other furnaces. As a result two factories saved tens of thousands of pounds a year on energy costs, none of which went back into the Unit's kitty, but the exercise strengthened Clark's position when asking for further annual budgets.

The largest project undertaken by the CRU in their first year was to persuade the Heating Division of Glynwed to look beyond their current range of boilers and conventional radiators. Their idea was to design a fan that could be plumbed into the hot water system from any kind of heat source – gas, solid fuel, electric or oil – and that would then convect the heat into the room. The compact box units would save wall space compared with the radiators they replaced (though they would stick out a little further) and the fans would distribute the heat more evenly about

Two versions of the CRU's fan-assisted domestic heating unit

the room. It sounded simple, but the problem with convectors had always been the noise of the fan, and to tackle this problem Clark tapped the resources of his old colleagues at Southampton University. Here already was an indication of the way in which the CRU was to supplement its own 'lean team': it would make use of every research institute in Britain, every library and every academic contact that might conceivably be able to help, and in so doing the Unit would solve – in a small way – that nagging British problem, how best to make use of government-funded research in order to create wealth for the nation. The list of institutions collaborating with the CRU at the time this book was being written included Reading University. (microbiology for water filtration), Birmingham (food technology, for their cookers), Oxford (engineering, for their turbine design), Bath (materials science for heat exchangers), Warwick (electrics), Newcastle (heat engines), Salford (electronics), and Strathclyde (home improvements).

With Southampton's assistance, and helped by Clark's own knowledge of noise and vibration, the team built their own reverberation chamber with instruments that could tell them exactly which part of the fan, which configuration, and which speeds were causing the trouble. As a result of their research and the improvements they achieved, it is possible to sit in the same room as one of the new convectors and be unaware that it is automatically hunting for the right fan speed to keep the room at the desired temperature, and unaware even that the fan is running. But Clark's problem in 1976 was the expense of this development: the market survey to establish that there would be sales for the new heater (how many central heating systems were installed in a year, how many old ones replaced, and so forth); development work, including the construction of the sound chamber; cost analysis, production design . . . The bill to the CRU amounted to £100,000 before they could begin to try and sell the heater to the division of Glynwed that would produce it. It was only with the greatest difficulty that Clark persuaded the Heating Division to invest the £35,000 needed to tool up for the new product. The 'client' promptly altered the neat, simple design conceived by Mike Rodger to a whole range of British nastiness, featuring beaten copper fascias, artificially flickering logs, a miniature garden – but that's British industry. At least the convector would appear on the market and that meant that here again Clark had successfully accounted for the Board's investment in the CRU. It was just as well, because the next £500,000 (the second year's budget) had to finance a list of projects that must have sounded even more outrageous to the directors than the first.

Take cookers. The Unit did not believe that the Aga – comfortable though its image most certainly was – represented the last word in cooking technology. They investigated the possibility of branching into microwave cookers, which were just arriving in full flood on the British market, but were unhappy on two counts. In the first place, there was continuing and growing evidence from the United States that microwaves were more dangerous than had been previously thought, and that safety standards would have to be increased (with greater cost to the consumer to cover the added precautions). Second, there was still consumer resistance due to the fact that microwaves cook quickly, but leave a certain amount to be desired when it comes to the look of the food. Microwaves cook by agitating the water molecules in the food very violently, and the agitation of one molecule heats its neighbours. In effect, this means that the food cooks from the inside out, with the result that the outside of the food is never brown. (Because there are no food molecules for the outer layer to agitate, the outside is in fact slightly cooler than the interior; the reason food in a conventional oven gets brown is that the outside is in fact the hottest part and the first to cook). Some dishes, such as chicken, actually seem to become a little parched on the outside. Microwaves, in short, serve some purposes very rapidly and efficiently, but they have their shortcomings.

The CRU therefore turned its attention back to conventional cookers, but with an eye on the fact that 60 per cent of the energy used by a conventional cooker is wasted (80 per cent in the case of the grill!), some because the heat escapes through the sides and top of the oven, but much because it is operating at wavelengths that do nothing to help cook the food. The cosy red glow of a gas burner or electric ring, for instance, has no effect at all on the

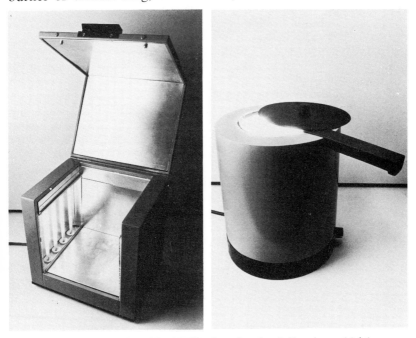

Development models of the CRU's infra-red cooker (left) and oven (right)

food; the only wavelength that actually cooks is confined to a small part of the infra-red; the visible red does nothing to help with the cooking!

So they turned their attention to the frequencies that were actually capable of doing the work. The first – and highly ingenious – idea was to arrange the infra-red elements in a vertical ring, creating a well of heat into which glass saucepans were lowered (glass, so that the rays could penetrate). The result of this design was that only the top of the saucepan was exposed to the outside air, and this gave the cooking plates a high degree of insulation – a design feature that conventional cookers could well follow. The team also experimented with techniques of pulsing the rays at different rates to achieve different kinds of cooking: a continuous burst of infra-red cooks the outside to a turn, while a slower pulse penetrates deep into the food. Microprocessor controls will eventually give the cook a failsafe method of using these techniques. The designs are very experimental at the time of writing, and as yet a long way from the market-place, but they are a good example of the kind of work that can be achieved by this kind of unit, with one eye on their costs and the market-place, and the other firmly on the long-term future of the company for which they work.

Because Clark was convinced the work he was doing would inevitably and increasingly involve the use of microelectronics, he persuaded the Board of Glynwed to perform an uncharacteristically buccaneering act. An electronics firm in Leeds – Fotherby and Willis – were in trouble following the crisis at Aston Martin (they had designed the microprocessor-controlled dashboard of the Lagonda) and were having difficulty in making ends meet from year to year. Clark saw the opportunity of wedding the experience of the Leeds firm to the work being done in his Unit and, sure enough, Glynwed purchased Fotherby and Willis and Clark had his microelectronics partner. From this collaboration sprang a range of alarms: a Doppler-controlled burglar alarm, a gas alarm using tin oxide, and an ionisation smoke alarm. A final extension of this brood was a car burglar alarm with a transmitter that activated a buzzer in the owner's pocket the moment his car was tampered with! At the time of writing, the CRU are working on a concept of a vandal-proof, all-electronic telephone exchange which they hope to sell to the Post Office.

Another of the Unit's less predictable moves took it into airbeds. Every year the Health Service spends £60 million treating long-stay patients for bedsores caused by lying in one position for long periods of time. A shifting bed surface could move the pressure point and prevent these sores, but the alternatives (such as hoverbeds at £2,500 a time) had proved too expensive. The

CRU's solution was an air mattress the top surface of which was arranged in a ribbed pattern of air-filled tubes stretched under the patient. Ribs one, three, five and so on were filled by a tiny compressor that pumped its air into the first of two airlines feeding every *other* tube in the mattress. An automatic rotating valve then, 15 seconds later, switched the air supply to the second airline, which fed ribs two, four, six and all the even numbers. The air from the odd numbers then escaped through tiny holes in the surface, which served the useful purpose of cooling the patient and reducing the perspiration sometimes caused by rubber mattresses. So for 15 seconds air poured into one bank of ribs, then for the next 15 that bank was allowed to deflate while the other bank became firm. The effect was a constantly rippling motion which ensured that no single part of the patient's body took his weight for very long. At the time of writing, the main problem still to be solved was the noise caused by the compressor: nobody would want to lie in a ward full of noisy machinery and so it's back to the reverberation chamber once more to try and sort out that problem.

The next job for the CRU will be to sell the airbed idea, presumably to Glynwed's Leisure Division (for whom the Unit is also developing a shower that can run for ever on just two gallons of water: chemical reagents in the sealed system cleanse and filter the permanently trapped supply). They go about marketing their ideas within the Group in a manner that could set an example to any designer trying to interest a sponsor, and which puts a high premium on the quality of their visual presentation. Every project on which they embark is not only researched and tested in the manner I have described, but it is also put forward in document form in the manner of the most elaborate American sales pitch. On one side of each of their 'Concept Reports' is a layman's guide to the concept, the market, the product and its advantages, with a photograph of the goods on offer. On the other side, in bold, 'handwritten' graphics, is a series of design jottings, a shorthand guide in words and pictures to the thought processes that went into the final product. In a sense, not unlike Tom French's original sketches and words which launched the Denovo, these reports provide the most technically illiterate of Board members or divisional managers with a simple, attractive guide to the virtues of the product the Unit has come up with.

And that's by no means all. One of the Unit's current projects, the hugely ambitious domestically fired heat pump, has no fewer than 10 graphically illustrated and well written brochures, introducing Board members to every aspect of the complicated technology, of the estimated market, and of production hurdles.

It's a long way from the sketch-on-the-back-of-an-envelope-

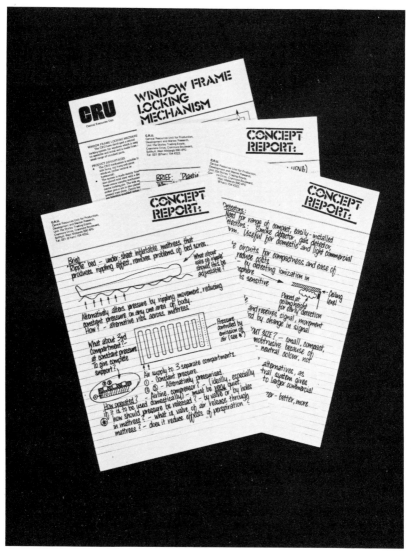

Some 'Concept Reports' produced for the CRU's Glynwed 'clients'

and-give-me-the-money approach that so many designers and engineers in Britain regard as more than enough to justify their funding. Clark, Hayward, and virtually every member of the Unit are highly articulate proponents of their work, anxious to communicate with outsiders rather than hide behind the jargon of their technologies. A cynic might say that this salesmanship is forced on them by the nature of the curious 'profit centre' philosophy Clark and Glynwed have bestowed on the Unit. Nobody in the CRU would have it any other way – marketing is in their blood.

It is Clark's ambition to extend the mandate of the Central Resources Unit beyond the (already pretty wide) limits set by their allegiance to the Glynwed Group. He believes that they could make a profit in the good old-fashioned sense of the word by hawking the Unit's skills on the open market, offering any taker the experience and facilities they have accumulated in Solihull, and in theory there is nothing to prevent him from taking this step. How it would work in practice is, however, less easy to see. Given a bright and challenging idea that fell outside the Glynwed brief, and then asked to lay aside this exciting concept in order to tackle some unglamorous problem – energy-saving for instance – that the Group wants it to solve, would the Unit's loyalty to Glynwed prevail?

How long would it be before the Unit's very success – assuming it came – expanded it beyond the intimate, 20-person scale at which it now works into the impersonal bureaucracy that so often comes with size? The present health of the CRU is tied very much to the personalities of one or two charismatic individuals, plus a happy set of management and technical circumstances. Growth in size could destroy the very essence of the Unit. It's a pity that the whole exercise can't simply be reproduced on the fringes of a number of other manufacturing conglomerates. But then, you'd have to hire the services of genetic engineers to clone the likes of Tony Hayward and Dr Ron Clark.

Chapter Eight

Venture Capitalists

No new design can prosper without the money needed to put it
into production. The case histories of four American
entrepreneurs who attempted to launch companies based on
brand new products . . . and the faith of their backers

America believes that the prosperity of the next generation
depends in large part on the innovators of today. Polaroid (instant
photography), Syntex (contraceptive pills), Intel (microprocessors), Digital Equipment Corporation (computers) and Xerox
(reprography) are just a few of the present generation of giants
based on scientific and engineering breakthroughs of the past
decade or so. IBM, Boeing and AT&T still loom large over
today's innovation scene because they have not forgotten that
they themselves started in this way. If countries in the so-called
Developed World are to compete with their rapidly industrialising
rivals in the Far East, Comecon and the rest, then – Americans
believe – it is only by keeping their technological noses ahead that
they will stay in the race.

This chapter and the next tell the tale of entrepreneurs on both
sides of the Atlantic who have attempted to found firms based on
new technology, and in particular their efforts to secure the
capital needed to finance their projects. The real reason why
Britain has given birth to perhaps only one successful company in
this category – Racal – while the American list is a long and
constantly growing one lies, I believe, very close to the ready
availability of venture capital in one country and its virtual
non-existence in the other.

For a start, America boasts a profession for which Britain has
virtually no equivalent – that of private Venture Capitalists. There
are around 500 such firms in the United States whose sole job it
is to finance new companies, and particularly those established to
exploit technical or scientific innovations. On top of that, many
of the large American commercial banks (the equivalent of
Britain's Big Four clearing banks) have specialised venture
capital arms called Small Business Investment Companies, whose

financial risks are underwritten by the Federal Government.

In the second place, America still possesses a healthy number of 'fat cats' – individuals lucky enough to have private wealth who are not only willing, but seemingly anxious, to invest in risky businesses. It's different over there: losses can be deducted from income tax, while investment gains are taxed at a much more lenient rate than other income. Americans appreciate that new enterprises create new jobs, and that the entrepreneur who makes himself a fortune is likely to benefit a lot of other people on the way. Thus is appears that there is little or no popular pressure to inhibit the accumulation of private wealth just so long as the money is likely to find its way back to provide other people with their livelihoods. New companies in particular are a tremendous boon to the economy; they employ a larger proportion of workers than many well established firms which have already reduced manning levels by introducing automated equipment. New companies also pay more tax, precisely because they have not yet been able to buy such capital-absorbing equipment and claim the cost against tax!

So in the United States there is a well established regiment of professional and amateur financiers ready and willing to invest money in new ventures. Furthermore, banking is organised on a purely state-by-state basis, and there is a good chance that any designer with a bright idea will find finance within arms's reach. It looks, from this side of the Atlantic, like Utopia.

But the boom-or-bust days of the late 1960s have gone; the times when it seemed that anyone could raise the wind for any kind of innovation, particularly if he was located near the famous Route 128 in Cambridge Massachussetts, or in California's Silicon Valley, the two most famous hot-houses for successful and some not-so-successful neophyte companies. Inflation and the US recession have hit venture capitalists as hard as they've hit other branches of business. Risk money is, as I've said, there to be secured, but to secure it the entrepreneur has to work like blazes.

Take the example of John Artley. John was in advertising, way back in 1971, when he came across a couple of scientists at Princeton University who had developed what seemed to Artley to be a novel and potentially profitable technology. Optical Character Recognition is the computerman's buzzword for machines that can recognise letters and numbers; in the broadest sense of the word, they can read. Because computers cannot react to shapes, lines or curves in their raw state, the challenge of Optical Character Recognition has been to convert visual material which the human eye can interpret without difficulty into the simple on-off (digital) code that computers can understand. The difficulties have, up to the time of writing, proved so great that while computers have relieved countless ledger clerks of their tedious (and expensive) number-crunching jobs, because calculations come easy to a computer, there are thousands of human operatives still doing equally tedious (and expensive) jobs that rely on reading or on character recognition rather than on mathematics, and up to now computers have not been able economically to replace the humans. The kind of job Artley reckoned OCR equipment could handle was that of checking that a sachet containing vegetable soup was in fact getting a label marked 'Vegetable Soup' and not one marked 'Tomato Soup'. It may sound trivial, but food firms quickly lose their reputation if they make too many such mistakes, and they do employ large numbers of people to check the system. Drug firms, of course, have to be especially careful that the right medicine is going into the right package, so it is not surprising that Artley's first customer turned out to be a pharmaceutical company.

The two scientists Artley met – one a pathologist, one a biologist – had been working since the mid-1960s on a system for calculating the areas bounded by the curves of letters and numbers written or printed on, let's say, a packet and checking these curves – now converted into digital information – against the letters and numbers contained in the computer's memory. The product they developed was based on a television Vidicon tube that scanned the object in front of it and reduced the picture to analogue curves, which in turn were sampled by the system's microprocessor and converted into digital information. This digital information could now be understood by the computer and matched against a 'feature set' – or in other words, the computer's idea of what the picture on the Vidicon tube should look like. Anyone who has looked at the curves on an oscilloscope fed by a television picture – and this, in essence, is the analogue of the television image – will have observed that those curves are absolutely unique to that one image, even if the picture is moving. This fact makes it possible for the OCR system to guarantee an absolutely precise match; if the curves are not identical, or near enough to satisfy the computer, then that fact can be registered instantly and a warning sounded. The system can be used to 'read' foreign languages: given a number of characters common to, let's say, invoices or despatch notes, it can scan the pages of Japanese or Arabic writing and register any characters it recognises. It can scan blood cells and spot abnormalities. It can check glass containers for the correct product label, provide 'sight' for industrial robots and, in time, will probably move into more and more areas of artificial intelligence.

Software theories are one thing, hardware products are another – particularly when the original designers are not computer men themselves! The development period· for the scientists' system was from 1972 to 1976, during which time the financial climate became harsher and harsher, and Artley today reckons that development took longer because money was so hard to raise. Nonetheless, raise it they did. In all, development cost $500,000 and it cost them $50,000 to raise that capital. They did it by means of a very careful and professional series of presentations aimed at the 'fat cats' and bankers of Boston and New York. The heart of the sales drive was a market survey of the business, to answer what would inevitably be the first questions posed by any potential investors: how many firms were likely to buy a system like the one Object Recognition Services (their new name) were offering; at what prices; what rivals were either in the field or likely to enter; what size of workforce and what rate of production did they contemplate; and had they a set of alternative plans to cope with unpredicted fluctuations in the market?

Once the market survey consultants and the ORS team felt confident that they could answer such questions, they invited specially selected, wealthy investors-to-be to sumptuous receptions at the best clubs in either Boston or New York. After luncheon, the guests were given a snappy slide and flip-chart presentation by the marketing consultants, by the scientists, and then by Artley himself, and they were invited to ask any questions. The optical character recognition equipment was there for them to experiment with and, in the best tradition of this kind of venture capitalism, the questions were often penetrating and always well informed.

By November 1973, ORS had raised its half million dollars in this manner from 14 private investors, and this money enabled them to commission further development work on their system at the University of Virginia. Here is another characteristic of the American scene – universities (which exist to make a profit) willing to do contract research and development work at competitive rates. Other faculties could have delivered the goods faster than Virginia, but ORS were compelled to go for their low tender and to wait a little while the pattern recognition scientists on the campus refined and de-bugged the system.

More money – $30,000 – went to secure US patent rights and some foreign protection. Artley and his colleagues had to debate long and hard whether to file for patents at all in a field in which it is not unknown for rivals to take advantage of computer programmes published in the patent application by simply changing a few of the algorithms so as to benefit from development work while managing not to infringe the patent itself. Today, they tend not to file for patents but to rely on the complexity of their software to protect their products.

While the Virginia team were steadily improving the ORS system, the whole project received its biggest single push forward by dint of Intel's introduction of the 8008, the first microprocessor. This meant a considerable reduction in both size and expense for the equipment involved. (Artley's rivals still rely on quite large computers for their optical character recognition, some as large as the IBM 370.) The two scientists whose idea set Artley up in business are now sleeping partners. They never wanted to be full-time businessmen, and they are happy to let Artley secure their share of the profits.

Now Object Recognition Services is ready for phase two of financing – $1 million and up. In November 1977 the first ORS system was installed at the Pfizer pharmaceutical plant in Brooklyn, monitoring batch numbers and expiration dates on labels. Artley expects the next round to come, at least in part, from the First National Bank of Boston, whom he has been 'prepping' and who have a healthy reputation for funding new ventures. Already ORS is ready to move into Europe and Artley has been assessing the prospects of investing in Europe with European money.

At the time of writing he is aware that he faces two dangers: he could over-invest in production equipment to meet what he believes will be a boom market, and then be faced with a slump or the emergence of an unexpectedly strong competitor (at present there is no market leader in this field); or he could be too cautious and miss out on a strong demand. Whether he succeeds or fails, ORS will have illustrated that in America it is possible for a lone entrepreneur to raise venture capital on a radically new technology – but that to do so he has to be very professional indeed in his approach to the investors.

The mood of American financiers has shifted from being bullish about start-up capital back in the late 1960s to preferring in the late 1970s to back partially established companies. The reasons they give are many. Pension funds, for instance, have been scared away from venture capital by the so-called 'Prudent Man' rule, which has recently been upheld by cautious fund managers as a reason why they should not invest in risky businesses – in theory, they could be prosecuted if they were found to be making investments that 'a prudent man' would not make, and start-ups could, they think, come into this category. Then there has been a distinct cutting back in public trading of new companies. In the heydays, it was easy for a venture capitalist to realise his profits fairly quickly by taking his company 'over the counter', a form of mini stock exchange that hardly exists in Britain but used to trade happily in companies far too small for the major exchanges of New York and the West Coast. With the recession came a decline in the number of brokers, and a lack of interest among the remaining ones in handling small accounts – precious few new companies traded from 1976 to 1978 and there were many failures, even among spectacularly successful ones, to raise the quotations they deserved. This in turn meant that the venture capital firms found themselves married to their investments for much longer than they might have wished – and therefore, as in human relationships, they were anxious to check the credentials of their applicants and less willing to form partnerships in the uncertain early days of seed money and start-ups.

At least, that is the theory, and as I write it is widely bruited in the more established investment companies of New York and even Boston and, through them, in the American press. In reality, there is start-up money to be found in America, if not in plenty then at least in quantities that would make most British entrepreneurs pale with envy. The story of Qume illustrates the success with which this seed money is being invested.

The man behind Qume is a venture capitalist called Paul Wythes, a partner in Sutter Hill, which is the investment subsidiary of the Canadian construction giant Genstar. Genstar have turned some $40 million of their capital assets over to form a 'basket fund' with the express purpose of taking spectacular risks and investing in start-ups. Sutter Hill's office suite is situated in the heart of new-technology land – California's Palo Alto, better known perhaps as Silicon Valley, where hundreds of computer and microprocessor firms have risen from the rich earth in the past decade. Sutter Hill's performance has been impressive: about four times the compound interest, reckons Wythes, that most conventional investment companies secured in the 1970s, and certainly five times the Dow Jones Index over the period. What makes these figures remarkable is the fact that Sutter Hill specialises in starting up new companies.

Paul Wythes had in a sense been involved in the Qume story before the company was formed in 1973. Back in the late 1960s he had funded the start-up of another company called Diablo, which was founded to manufacture disc drives for high-speed computers. The design skills required to manufacture these depended above all on the ability to produce the best possible servo mechanism to start, stop, accelerate and decelerate the equipment at speeds greater than those achieved by Diablo's rivals. One of the key designers in the Diablo project was also the second crucial figure in the Qume story, David Lee. Lee – one of his ancestors is said to have introduced Peking Duck to America – is a brilliant electronics designer, and when the Diablo team had successfully designed and launched their disc drive, Lee was part of the team that looked around for another product to design. The idea they struck was the Daisy Wheel.

The Daisy Wheel is, in a sense, a typewriter on a stem. It consists of a rimless wheel or flower with 96 petals, at the end of each of which is a letter, a number or a punctuation mark. The wheel rotates at high speed until it stops at the desired character, and then a small hammer head comes from behind the wheel and taps it against a ribbon and the page. It is, in effect, a two-dimensional version of the famous IBM rotating golf ball, and is capable of moving even faster.

The Daisy Wheel in itself was not a new idea; in fact, it had been around for some 13 years and an old patent existed on the primitive outline design. Nobody, however, had succeeded in designing a drive mechanism that could stop, start, accelerate and decelerate the wheel at the speeds required to out-perform the golf ball, nor were there plastics or other materials both strong and flexible enough to withstand the speeds involved. Diablo could not have made their choice at a more opportune time: new plastics arrived on the market in the early 1970s strong enough to take the stress of stopping and starting at speeds of around 30 characters a second; what was more, microprocessors were now being produced right there in Silicon Valley that reduced both the size and the cost of the drive mechanism. Lee and the others applied their experience with servo mechanisms and computer technology to these two happy new arrivals and, in 1972, Diablo announced their first Daisy Wheel Printer.

The next event took everyone by surprise, though with the advantage of hindsight it is possible to see how logical it all was. At the time Diablo made their announcement, the computer printer market was dominated by the IBM golf ball, and IBM's competitors had other reasons, apart from better performance, for welcoming a newcomer in the printer field. IBM were after all 'original equipment manufacturers', which meant that they did not simply manufacture components – such as the golf ball – that could be sold to their rivals, but they also made computers. This meant that other computer manufacturers had to suffer the indignity of having to buy components from one of their most powerful rivals in order to build their own equipment. Diablo's arrival with a new printer was welcomed with a huge sigh of relief, in that here was a firm that *only* made components from whom other computer firms could buy a better printer and release themselves from their dependence on IBM for this piece of equipment.

But not for long. Diablo announced their Daisy Wheel in April 1972, to be confronted almost immediately by 'an offer they couldn't refuse' – a bid of $29 million by the mighty Xerox Corporation, one of IBM's rivals – and not just of money but of Xerox stock, one of the blue-chip investments of the day. A bid of $29 million for a company that had only been founded three years earlier! Paul Wythes and his partners had little trouble reaching their decision and the company was handed over to Xerox early that summer. It was at this point that Xerox made what Wythes describes as 'a dramatic mistake'.

It is the custom in this kind of take-over that the purchasing corporation identifies the key personnel in the company it acquires and then either ties them to good jobs and long contracts, or at least buys them out of that particular technology for so many years that it need not feel threatened by the prospect of their skills being employed to compete in the same market-place. Xerox duly tied up the President of Diablo, George Constock, and other executives and technical experts. The only person they neglected, it seems, was David Lee.

Lee did not in fact realise what Xerox had failed to do for quite some time. Chagrined by the fact that Xerox were bringing line managers in above him in a move that he feels today was a distinct demotion, he started asking around and only then discovered that most of his colleagues had been favoured – or bound – by exclusive contracts. Hurt, David Lee presented himself one morning that summer in Paul Wythes's office with the proposition that Sutter Hill provide start-up money for a new company to be founded on David Lee's ability as a designer and on one of a list of new products he had with him, at the head of which was another printer design, this time for a paper printer for small desk-top calculators.

Wythes agreed with the idea of forming a company around David Lee's design talent, but not with the concept of a printer for calculators. Rightly or wrongly it was his information that the Japanese had a clear lead in this kind of concept, and he believed that Lee's abilities would be better geared to – of all things – another Daisy Wheel. Wythes's reasoning was simple. Xerox had, by buying Diablo, put themselves in substantially the same position as the one that had long been occupied by IBM – that of an original equipment manufacturer with a monopoly over a key component. In fact his continuing contacts with Diablo indicated to Wythes that there was a possibility that Xerox were going to restrict sales of the Daisy Wheel in order to give their own products a distinct advantage in the field. He therefore agreed that Sutter Hill would underwrite Lee on condition that the first product of the new company – Qume – would be a new Daisy Wheel.

The task facing Lee was not an easy one, as later events confirmed. He had to produce a new Daisy Wheel that would be sufficiently different from the Diablo model to make it difficult for Xerox to sue the new company. He did this, first, by producing a much faster wheel than Diablo – the Qume model achieves nearly twice the speed of the Diablo, averaging 60 characters a second. Then he introduced refinements made possible partly by the ever-improving technology of microprocessors, such as a control over ribbon movement so that the ribbon only moved on by the space occupied by the character being used. Six different hammer pressures are available on the Qume printer compared with only two on the Diablo, giving a much more elegant end product, with characters printed at precisely the correct strength. This refinement gave Qume a tremendous strength in the new market that was just beginning, in the early 1970s, to give the Daisy Wheel a fresh and important outlet – that of Word Processing.

Word Processing replaces a vast amount of office keyboard work with electronics. Instead of early drafts of documents being typed on paper, a word processing operative keys the figures and letters directly into a computer memory, with a visual display unit displaying the text so that first the operative and then the person who dictated the document can scan and correct the content. It is extremely easy to correct either single words or whole passages of the text – the computer can shift or erase with no trouble at all – and the final step, when everyone is content, is simply to press the 'print' button, and the document comes out as fast as the printer will allow. In law firms, which have to handle large numbers of nearly identical documents, or in insurance

The Qume Daisy Wheel

companies with standard policies to issue, it is extremely easy to key in minor amendments to each basic text and print out contracts at high speed.

The word processing industry was delighted to see the higher quality of print, as well as the greater speed, offered by the new Qume wheel when it appeared, and for this reason Qume have always claimed that their primary market – and therefore their product – was sufficiently different from Diablo's not to be a case of simple piracy. But before the product could be launched there was another clause in the Sutter Hill provisions to be met, and this was Paul Wythes's insistence that Qume attract and employ a president capable of running the company. Both men agreed that David Lee was not the presidential type (to this day, he doesn't really understand the financing and isn't fully aware what his own holding in Qume is) and that the company would need a strong executive at the helm. This in itself reflects perhaps the strongest single difference between the American and the British ways of launching new ventures. The British financier neither wants nor feels free to get involved at such a personal and detailed level with small companies; the British entrepreneur, in his turn, resents interference at this kind of level and is loath to feel that he is being 'manipulated' by the money men. Between the two a great void has appeared, with financier and designer/inventor glowering across it at each other with mutual suspicion.

In America it is taken for granted both that the original entrepreneur may not be capable of running his own show and that the financier should play an active role in deciding who is. As one New York financier put it to me, 'It's like music: the virtuoso violinist may do fine as a soloist or leading a small ensemble, but when you're dealing with something the size of an orchestra then the most brilliant player may not be the man to keep the whole show together. That's when we should bring in a new conductor.' So it was with Qume: Wythes had already decided what product they should manufacture and now he helped select the man to run the company. The new president was Bob Schroeder, until then the man in charge of the New Products Group of Cummings Engineering, one of the big US companies, but who wanted to branch out on his own. Enticed both by the prospect of a completely new venture and by the prospect of an equity stake in the company, Schroeder took a drop in salary, sold his holiday home, took his children out of private school and joined Qume as President.

At this point, Wythes effectively ended his close involvement with Qume. He had already 'quarter-backed' the first round of investment – Sutter Hill had put up $300,000, they had persuaded an East Coast investor to put in the same amount, and the founders – including the new president – were allocated the remaining $100,000. Now, with the company both launched and staffed at the top, Wythes left it to Schroeder to handle the next round. This time, interestingly, the principal shareholder turned out to be Exxon, or Esso as they were once called, fast becoming a major investor in new technologies and especially those concerned with the word processing field. There has been some speculation that Exxon are looking to the day when it will be more economical to transport facts and texts electronically than to burn oil in ferrying human passengers from one meeting to another, and that they are preparing for the day when oil is no longer a powerful enough commodity on which to base a corporation of their size. Their involvement is also an indication of Big Business's increasing role where the new-technology companies are concerned. There may no longer be the option of trading companies 'over the counter', but most venture capitalists are becoming skilful in attracting revenue from corporations to replace public quotation as a means of making their profits.

But if round two went through smoothly with a little help from the large corporation, round three was almost wrecked by the direct interference of another big boy. With only days to go before signatures were due, in June 1973, during the third round of financing, Xerox announced that they were going to sue Qume for piracy of ideas and personnel. Schroeder and all at Qume had a very unpleasant few weeks reassuring the would-be investors. To everybody's credit the investors, with only a couple of exceptions, stood firm and the round was only delayed by three weeks, which was just as well because the ensuing court action was to be extremely expensive for Qume. It was a David and Goliath situation, as Wythes puts it, but the costs falling on David's shoulders hurt the small company a lot more than they did the giant Xerox corporation. Nobody really seems to have won the action, which ironically benefitted both parties because no one can now enter the Daisy Wheel field without taking a licence from either Xerox or Qume, so the field is now effectively a protected one. Qume, in turn, pay a licence fee to Xerox, but they are free to produce their printers, and produce they do, very effectively. In the calendar year of 1977 they increased their staff from 300 to 1,300; their annual sales, which started in 1974 at $10,000, hit $40,000,000 in 1977/8 and are expected to top $100,000,000 in 1978/9. It is, says Wythes today, the single most spectacular venture capital story of the 1970s, and a tribute to some fine buccaneering and some perceptive decisions by the people on both sides of the financier's desk.

The perils and the success stories in this field spill over one another, particularly in California. To round off this account of venture capital in the USA it is interesting to compare the status of two companies both operating in the most difficult of all the risk businesses – the medical field. One company is now positively geriatric· by Silicon Valley standards – it celebrated its tenth birthday in 1978 – while the other had not even finished building its production line by the end of the same year.

Alza is named after its founder, Alex Zaffaroni, a Uruguayan medical student who went to the USA to study at the University of Rochester and was then persuaded to go to the West Coast to join Syntex, at that time a fairly small operation, but one which blossomed during Zaffaroni's period there. When he left, in 1968, Syntex was worth $75 million and Zaffaroni was able to take with him quite a sizeable nest egg with which to realise the dream he had been nurturing – the concept of targeted drugs.

Zaffaroni's reasoning was that the 'pharmacopoeia', the inventory of known drugs, was by now so full that it took a major corporation with a research budget of hundreds of millions of dollars to discover and launch a new drug, but he felt that innovation was possible by looking, not at new drugs, but at new methods of delivering existing ones. 'We model ourselves on the body itself', says Zaffaroni; 'The endocrine gland, for instance, releases its own hormones in small regular doses over the required period. When we take medicines, we tend to behave like the first guests at a cocktail party who drink the whole house dry in the first hour – we consume too much in one batch, and then have to remain dry till the next dose.'

Zaffaroni's first design – which was his own idea – was a method of delivering medicine to the eye in even, regulated doses. The Ocusert is a transparent plastic sandwich with a layer of medicine in the middle. It is placed under the bottom lid of the eye, where it does not interfere with vision, and sits there for a week, releasing the drug through the porous plastic at an absolutely regular rate; better by far, claim Alza, than deluging the eye every few hours with massive doses with nothing in between.

So it was with the next product, the Progestasert. The idea here was that most of the side-effects of the contraceptive pill are caused, both because far too much hormone is taken by the woman, and because a lot of that hormone ends up in the wrong parts of the stomach. The Progestasert is an intra-uterine device that releases minute quantities of progesterone to precisely the right part of the body – the womb – where it can have the intended effect. During a whole year the Progestasert releases only as much hormone as the daily pill contains in three doses.

Zaffaroni brought these and other devices like them to the market by building in Palo Alto one of the most imaginative and best equipped research teams ever assembled in an industrial setting. Eleven buildings, some specially built and very attractive indeed (the headquarters in Page Mill Road won an architectural award), contain some of the finest equipment and decorations money can buy (Zaffaroni's own collection of painting and sculpture adorns the head-office building). Meals are subsidised, in the hope that lunch-times will serve to bring scientists from different disciplines together to discuss fresh ideas and to cross the departmental boundaries that act as powerful deterrents to innovation in many scientific establishments.

And the ideas kept coming in. A chemical engineer and a mechanical engineer, both working in fluidics, combined with a biologist and a chemist to produce one of Alza's most ingenious designs, a pump in a pill known as the Oros. The idea here was to prevent the single bombardment the stomach receives when it takes a conventional pill – like the eye drops, a pill arrives every four or eight hours and deluges the stomach lining, which then has to wait an extended period before the next dose arrives. The Oros is a pill whose outer coating is a semi-permeable membrane, which means that the body's fluids can get in but can't escape. The drug is packaged in soluble form inside the membrane, and it duly dissolves when the fluid seeps in, causing a space problem – the fluid has expanded the contents inside the membrane and something has to give. Escape is provided by a tiny hole etched by a laser in the exterior of the pill and the size of this hole dictates exactly the rate at which the medicine will escape, typically spreading its release over just 24 hours, or the period it takes the pill to pass through the digestive tract.

One remarkable feature of the Alza Corporation is the fact that it raised no less than $100 million by the end of 1977 without even showing a sign of realising a profit on any of its products. Zaffaroni was not disheartened, pointing out that the life sciences field is not like computers, where new products come and go without overheads and where – as in the case of the Daisy Wheel – rivals can pick a company off the moment it has a good product. It takes a long time to achieve innovation in the medical field, not least because even after a firm has convinced itself that a product is effective, it has still got to satisfy the Food and Drugs Administration in the US and its equivalent in every other country that the product is entirely without dangers, and this can add a good four years to the product development schedule. At the end of 1977 there was a scare in Britain when Alza's own figures were held to have proven that if a pregnancy did occur in a woman who had been using the Progestasert (and no form of contraceptive is 100 per cent effective) then there was a slightly higher chance of that pregnancy being ectopic – occurring in the neck of the womb – than was normal. That's the kind of scare that can add years to a development schedule, and at the time of writing Alza are awaiting the results of subsequent FDA hearings.

There has been a further snag with the Alza products, however, and this one severely impairs their chance of being profitable. None of their target delivery systems is 'uniquely necessary'. Unlike the new wonder drug that patients queue up to buy, a new form of drug delivery – especially one that adds to already large medical bills – is going to take a low place on the list of priorities of most doctors. It is possible to cure the patient without relying on these new systems and, as Alza's finance director put it, what doctor ever stops to think about the possibility of patients who forget to take their pills (or worse, about the patients who forget that they *have* taken their pills – and take another dose an hour later, for luck!)?

At this point it is worth mentioning that the Alza story lacks one key member of the dramatis personae of this chapter – a venture capitalist. The finance director I have just quoted is Martin Gerstel, a good-looking graduate of Stanford Business School who has been in charge of finance at Alza since he left Stanford, and the company was formed, in 1968. In their time, Zaffaroni and Gerstel have dreamed up some ingenious forms of raising new finance, such as offering marketing licences in exchange for equity. Much of the original money was Zaffaroni's own investment, the result of his prosperous period at Syntex, and the style and personality of the elegant South American have played a great part in convincing other investors that Alza was an exciting prospect. When a book was written in the mid-1970s by Gene Bylinsky called *The Innovative Millionaires*, Alex Zaffaroni and Alza had a chapter to themselves, and tribute was paid to the fact that he had achieved all this without the help of the professionals.

Well, by the end of 1977 Alza's luck ran out. There was no way they could survive another three months without a fresh injection of capital, and no prospect at all that the product line would suddenly begin to show a profit. When Ciba Geigy offered what Zaffaroni describes as 'an arrangement' whereby $35 million would in effect buy them control of the company, there was no way that Zaffaroni could refuse – as the Turkish proverb has it, 'the drowning man clutches at the serpent'. In fact, Ciba Geigy were taking only the smallest of risks: Alza had been rated as a tax loss amounting to $30,000 which Ciba Geigy could, if they wanted, off-load against their investment. For the rest, they had secured some of the finest research premises and staff in the world, and it was as a research and development arm that they intended to run Alza.

The staff of the company are only too happy that the company is not going to fold – because this was the all too apparent nightmare of 1977 – while Zaffaroni himself is philosophical about his failure. 'It was', he says, 'the biggest single capital undertaking in the history of American venture capital.' And he could have added that it was all achieved outside the institutions and the offices of the professionals. He is still doing the work he enjoys and in fact he has launched other, smaller companies, based on similar biological models to the target delivery systems of Alza.

In the meantime, undeterred by the fall of their mighty neighbour, four medics spent 1978 getting their brand new company off the ground with a product as unpredictable as any of Alza's, giving the lie to premature rumours that venture capital, especially start-up money, was not to be found any more. Collagen Corporation is backed by a venture capitalist – in fact until April 1978 it was actually run by one, as we shall see – and at the time of writing it has only one full-time executive. On paper, it looks like a real 'ball of wax' – as one of the founders described it – yet you won't find any of the participants prepared to admit a serious chance of failure.

It was at a neighbourhood party that Rodney Perkins, an ear specialist, mentioned to his friend Reid Dennis that he had become involved in an intriguing new project. It is by no means the textbook way for a venture capitalist to hear of an investment possibility, but then Reid Dennis does not worry much about the textbook. He has been in the business most of his life, running the American Express venture capital arm until in 1974, backed by a substantial investment from his old company, he set up Institutional Venture Associates in Menlo Park, one of the tributaries of Silicon Valley.

The story that Rodney Perkins told Reid Dennis was of John Daniels, an associate professor of oncology (cancer studies) at Stanford who happened to be talking one day with an ambitious young plastic surgeon, Terry Knapp, about the work Daniels had been doing in studying the body's rejection of skin tissue, or collagen, taken from animals. In fact, rejection is the wrong term, since it was well known that animal collagen could be 'purified' to a point at which the human body would do nothing to reject the foreign material, but the animal tissue then rendered no useful purpose to the host because it was incapable of regenerating itself. The very elements in animal tissue that control the structure of fibres, the telopeptides – basically a form of miniature junction box that hold the tiny fibrils together – are also, as luck would have it, the elements that cause the human body to reject any collagen it has not grown itself. Remove the telopeptides (which is not difficult, by means of an enzyme called pepsin which simply eats away the bonds) and the fibrils are made innocuous enough for the human body to accept them, but the structure of the collagen molecules is also reduced to such a loose state that they cannot re-form.

Exactly what emerged in that conversation between John Daniels and Terry Knapp is not clear – they have been keeping it a closely guarded secret ever since – but between them they evidently hit on a chemical formula that not only enabled them to take the hides of slaughtered calves, purify the animal tissue of all its telopeptides and other unacceptable material (that much is established science) but also – this is the magic – to use what they describe as a 'chemical magnet' to line the errant fibrils up in as perfect a tissue formation as if they were in their former state, complete with their telopeptide junction boxes. How it is done is uncertain, but there is clear evidence that their formula works. At 37°C – body temperature – the clear solution of randomly arranged collagen molecules goes milky and begins to thicken up. In the body, the animal collagen forms a lattice-work of new tissue that not only does a respectable repair job in its own right, but also encourages the human collagen to grow where it has previously failed to propagate, complete with blood vessels and all the supporting mechanisms of normal growth.

Around this discovery a small team immediately formed. Terry Knapp's expertise in plastic surgery made him instantly aware of the potential market for a means of curing skin blemishes, pock-marks, scars and wrinkles. John Daniels and he also thought of the possibility of using their injectable collagen to repair serious burns, which are currently treated either with superficial pig dressing or with very expensive grafts from dead humans. If the collagen could be persuaded to grow deep inside the body, then there was even the possibility of repairing damaged nerve tissues. Rodney Perkins, a wealthy doctor working in Palo Alto, was one of the first to hear of the work and being, like many American doctors, a wealthy man with money to spare, he was anxious to become involved in a project so close to his heart. Rodney Perkins's specialism was ear surgery and he had instituted a special research project to hunt for a membrane that could replace damaged tympanic tissues in the ear. A medical student working on this project, Ed Luck, had himself been working on solubilised collagen. All four men were based in Palo Alto, and around them Collagen Corporation was formed.

It was an unlikely team of people, with existing jobs to perform and no business experience at all. Until Rodney Perkins happened, at that fateful barbecue party back in 1975, to mention the new venture to his friend Reid Dennis, the Corporation lacked both adequate finance and any form of management expertise. Reid Dennis was the ideal man to supply both.

Today he seems occasionally to regret the impulse that led him to underwrite this 'pony and dog show'. Although his company's investment of \$590,000 in Collagen Corporation only represented one and a half per cent of IVA's total portfolio, Reid Dennis found that over a third of his working life was devoted to running the company in his unofficial – and unwanted – role of part-time president. His IVA partners thought him crazy to get involved, but Reid Dennis is the kind of man who, to put it mildly, enjoys a challenge – whether it is piloting one of his three twin-engined planes across the Atlantic to see his son at school in England, or motoring his superbly maintained 20-year-old Aston Martin in and out of the freeway traffic, or proving to the world that a crazy notion like Collagen Corporation could, even in the wake of Alza's failure, be made to work and to net a huge profit from the lucrative American plastic surgery market.

Throughout 1976 and 1977, John Daniels and Ed Luck worked all the hours they could find (supported by hired scientists) to produce a large enough inventory of the injectible collagen to see them through clinical trials of the material. At the end of 1977 they took possession of new industrial premises not far from Stanford and immediately set about clean-room preparation and packaging of the material they had produced, shipping it out (at a charge) to doctors whom they could include in their trials. There was no way during that year in which they could produce more collagen, because they now had no production line – and they didn't dare invest in a new production line until they knew for sure that the collagen would prove clinically acceptable.

In the meantime, Reid Dennis was still acting as president of Collagen Corporation. It was a desperate situation until April that year, when he managed to find a replacement acceptable to the founders and willing to cope. Ironically, the person they appointed as president was Howard Palefsky, who had been in charge of Alza's marketing, and who now knew all there was to know about selling new products in the medical field.

At the time this book was being written it was far too soon to know whether the Collagen story would emerge as a success or a failure. John Daniels was undecided whether to remain as part-time academic researcher and part-time industrialist, or to abandon cancer study and become full-time entrepreneur. But Collagen Corporation stands or falls a tribute both to the willingness of Stanford University to 'share' its staff with mammon, and indeed to provide the research back-up needed to launch collagen as a product, and to a venture capitalist who was willing, while all about him in the medical field were losing their nerve, to stand his ground and put money and a lot of time into one of the riskiest businesses of them all. As any British innovator will know, it couldn't happen here.

Chapter Nine

Turtles' Eggs

The British experience: the desperate hunt for risk capital
and for financiers who understand new technologies and
are prepared to put their faith in entrepreneurs and
their companies

On a remote beach in Trengganu, Malaya, I once witnessed the extraordinary sight of giant turtles laying their eggs. They crawl ponderously across the sand, select their spot, then dig a deep hole with their flippers. Into this cavity they lay perhaps 100 ping-pong-ball-sized eggs, then fill the hole with sand and crawl back to the ocean. In time, perhaps 10 of these eggs will hatch, and possibly just one baby turtle will actually reach the sea to face the still smaller chances of survival in the deep.

So it is with small companies trying to get innovative products off the ground in Britain. By definition, new businesses of this kind are risk-laden and, of the hundreds of such products that are conceived, many will not survive technical development, others will be simply too expensive, some will not be wanted in the market-place, and more will turn out to be good ideas but identical to products developed simultaneously by rival firms.

But British turtles' eggs have one more threat to their survival, in that there will be a distinct lack of sustenance when the neophyte company gets down the sand to the water's edge. Britain's private venture capitalists are conspicuous by their scarcity, while the institutions often seem to be so, well, institutional that the entrepreneur can be forgiven for feeling that he is an embarrassing nuisance whom they wish would go away.

The premise upon which the American venture capital business is based is the belief that without small innovative companies today there will be a lack of large prosperous corporations tomorrow, and that in particular the new-technology firms play more than their proportionate role in supplying both jobs and revenue to assist the national exchequer. University and industrial research departments alike seem to be filled with aspiring would-be entrepreneurs planning the first chapter of their future autobiography, entitled *The Next Xerox*, and polishing the small print on the patent specifications and marketing plans for the invention they believe will make their fortune.

Britain *must* have its share of innovators: since the war we have produced more Nobel laureates than America (per head of population) and the 'Tomorrow's World' programme would have died years ago without its steady diet of original designs and ingenious prototypes. Nor is there any shortage of money available for investment; any banker will tell you that his problem is finding not the cash but projects in which to invest. 'We make money by making loans', said one financier, 'not by *not* making loans.' So the problem seems to be one of mutual confidence; it seems the governments of Brazil or Zaire have only to pick up a telephone to secure a multi-million pound loan from London's hallowed Golden Mile, and property speculators have seldom found it difficult to raise the wind with which to sweep aside another town centre, but the man with a high-technology project finds it difficult to get through the door, and almost impossible to find anyone inside who understands exactly what his innovation has to offer.

This chapter looks first at the finance houses whose business it should be to provide venture capital here in Britain, and then at two entrepreneurs who have run the full gamut of these institutions and failed to secure any support whatsoever from the traditional British sources of risk finance. Happily, however, both companies are alive and prospering today, despite the lack of that all-important early support.

Harold Wilson was President of the Board of Trade when, in 1948, he introduced in Parliament the Bill that established the National Research Development Corporation, the body which today represents Britain's main effort to evaluate, and if possible to finance, new technologies. The NRDC employs a technical staff of 45 and a further 15 patent experts whose job it is to assess the market and production potential of any prototype brought to them. The mainstream of ideas coming to the NRDC is from government-financed laboratories; it is specified in the contract of every scientist or engineer working in a university or a public research body that work must be taken to the NRDC if it is potentially of commercial value. It was from this source that the highly profitable antibiotic Cephalosporin came to the NRDC, and this family of drugs has so far earned the agency no less than £50 million, which in turn accounts for the fact that the NRDC was able in 1977 to declare a profit of £10 million and the intention of increasing its investment in new technologies from its current annual figure of £4·4 million to £5 or even £6 million. It was from another government laboratory, as we have seen, that Dr Majumdar brought his discovery of Alkali Resistant Glass, on the licence of which the NRDC expects once again to score heavily.

But for every scientist with an NRDC success to report there are hundreds complaining, rightly or wrongly, that the agency took so long to reject their project that the discovery had lost its lead time and any chance of success. The number of ideas the NRDC has to consider in its unsolicited monopoly role is enormous and delays in the important evaluation stages are perhaps the most common complaint levelled against the agency.

Apart, that is, from outright rejection. No inventor can easily accept that his idea is less than brilliant, and the reception area of the NRDC's headquarters building in London's Victoria is constantly filled with earnest pioneers showing patient and courteous staff the exercise books in which they have scrawled their designs for perpetual motion machines or their conquest of the second law of thermodynamics. The NRDC is obliged to assess private innovations as well as the work of government scientists, and in this field it is only too well aware that its record is far from perfect. We shall see how Arthur Crump of Spectronics felt himself to be starved of the necessary funds, even though his design had been accepted on technical grounds, and how he received his payments too slowly, while having to pay a very high fixed interest rate. Perhaps such delays are caused by the agency's need to be civil to all comers. Perhaps the NRDC tries to lend to too many enterprises, and in doing so spreads its financial jam too thinly to be of real use to the companies it does eventually back. Whatever the cause, the back-of-envelope designers end up with little love for the NRDC, despite the fact that in many cases neither they nor their designs were ever in the least likely to succeed. In 23 years the corporation has given its careful consideration to no fewer than 23,000 submissions and it points to the fact that only 37 of these have become profitable as proof that Britain is, in its opinion, short of good ideas.

The tragedy of the NRDC is its isolation; the fact that there is only one of it. Its total portfolio, currently running at around £45 million, is actually slightly less than the combined investments made by just two of the private firms we met in Silicon Valley USA – Paul Wythes's Sutter Hill and Reid Dennis's IVA. If the NRDC could concentrate its attention on fewer companies (at present it has holdings in well over 200 ventures, which means that three quarters of these have loans of less than £50,000), and above all if it could then emulate the Americans in supplying not only cash but also management expertise to the aspiring entrepreneur, it might itself be surprised at the increase in the number of success stories it would have to tell. At present it, like so many British financiers, expects the innovator to be management genius and businessman as well. The good news is that the NRDC acknowledges its shortcomings and is trying very hard indeed to remedy the situation.

As I have said, it would be easier if there were other bodies capable of taking some of the load away from the NRDC. At the start-up stage there are precious few firms ready to supply money to new companies, and fewer still capable of assessing advanced technologies. The Small Business Capital Fund, for instance, prides itself on helping the entrepreneur, but it too claims that it cannot find the ventures worth supporting. Supported by the Co-operative Insurance Company, it has a portfolio of just £6 million and says it can lay its hands on more if the need arises. It has a few fairly risky technologies on its books, but the bulk of its holdings are in service companies or well established industries. Then, after the SBCF, comes a tiny handful of private investment companies prepared to put money into start-ups, with probably less than £10 million to spare between them. The NEB, as we shall see, has a small role to play here, but a rough calculation indicates that there is less start-up money available in the whole of Britain than in Silicon Valley, in Cambridge Massachussetts, or in any one of a number of American financial centres. There is no single villain; the tragedy for the innovator trying to set up on his own in Britain is that the cupboard is so very, very bare.

One institution that could take the strain off the other venture capitalists is the Industrial and Commercial Finance Corporation – ICFC – set up in 1945 on the basis of 15 per cent investment by the Bank of England and 85 per cent by the Clearing Banks of England and Scotland. The ICFC has a subsidiary – the Technical Development Corporation – whose specific job is to invest in new technologies, but whose record is frankly shameful. It has invested £16·5 million (still a drop in the American ocean) in 277 new companies, of which 157 are still trading and 93 have failed completely. In only 10 cases has the TDC actually made a profit, though there may be some unrealised profits out there, biding their time. It all compares rather dismally with the ICFC's record of investment in less risky projects; at 31 March 1977 the mighty corporation had £212 millions invested in 2201 companies with particular emphasis on the small and medium-sized firms. There's nothing wrong with our record with small companies, says the ICFC, it's the new-technology firms that give us the headaches. And like all the other institutions mentioned so far, the ICFC claims that it turns away very few worthwhile entrepreneurs and that there is a distinct shortage of people with inspiring ideas beating paths to its door.

Something is obviously seriously wrong with a situation in which the men of ideas claim they can find nobody to listen to their proposals and the men of money claim there are no men of ideas to be found. The Governor of the Bank of England, Gordon Richardson, made an important speech at an ICFC conference in October 1977. In it he pointed an accusing finger at the 'administrative economies of scale which reinforce the natural tendencies of institutional directors towards investment in large companies'. In other words, the small and particularly the technically complex ventures are expensive to evaluate; putting in the necessary managerial back-up costs even more money, and it is simpler to invest in businesses and businessmen who can demonstrate by their proven track records that they are going to demand little attention from the investor. A senior official from the National Economic Development Office was harsher: institutions like the ICFC exist, he said, purely as conscience money in that they enable the banks to point to them and say 'We're making our contribution to venture capital through the money we have put into the ICFC. If it can't make a success of this kind of investment, how can you expect us to risk our depositors' money any further?' So what of the banks? It may seem strange to come so late to the place where most entrepreneurs would naturally start their hunt for funds – the local bank. Isn't the branch manager in the High Street the best man to support the enterprising local designer or inventor and to keep an eye on him and help him through his early struggles?

The answer is a categorical no. Britain's clearing banks are best described by an analogy they have created for themselves, that of a tree with a trunk and with branches radiating out from the centre. 'Our roots are our branches', claims one advertisement, but the description is financially misleading as well as botanically unsound. The further, in fact, one travels out from central control in the City of London, the less responsibility is permitted to the local manager and the less encouragement is he given to take risks with the bank's money. Bankers are seldom, as in America, recruited from the top stream of university graduates. They are not, as in America, strongly local in their decision-making organisation. American banks are forbidden to cross state boundaries and therefore the only way in which they can grow is by being fiercely competitive within their own area; the British scene is the precise opposite, and our banks sometimes seem more preoccupied with expanding overseas than in encouraging more enlightened investment at the local level. Lastly, whereas American banks operate informal investment counselling services encouraging local 'fat cats' to join them in new ventures, and the riskier the better, the British High Street banker is trained to evaluate every potential investee on his track record, his solidity in the community, and above all on his collateral. An entrepreneur, especially if he is new to industry, will have to put his personal assets – his house included – on the line if he is going to borrow from his local bank, and he will receive little or no front-line advice. Here's Gordon Richardson again: 'I believe the banks do a good job in this matter, but out of 14,000 branch bank managers there are bound to be some who may seem less good than others in helping those running small businesses. I know the clearing banks are working to improve the training and knowledge of branch managers and I am certain also that they are giving thought to ways in which the organisation and techniques of decision-making in the fields of lending can be better adapted to the changing needs of industry and commerce.' If the Governor of the Bank of England seems there to be kinder to the clearing banks than he was to the institutions, it should be mentioned that he was talking of *all* small businesses, most of whom are in the service industries or in well established forms of manufacture – not just about our naked inventor or designer.

There are some encouraging signs of change. Until recently, Britain's attitude to lending was straightforward and pretty unhelpful to the man setting up in a venture with little chance of short-term profits; our depositors' money, said the banks, is on immediate recall, so our loans too should be equally liquid. This meant that they could foreclose on a bank loan just as soon as they lost confidence in the venture, and this would see very few firms through the troughs to which any new venture tends to fall prey. Now things are getting easier: of Barclays' loans to industry in general, 40 per cent are now medium term. In Germany and Japan (not to risk anger by quoting America yet again) *long*-term lending is a well established bank practice, and the British innovator must fervently hope that our banks will continue to move in this direction.

Furthermore, the clearing banks, sensitive to criticism of their performance in this area, are moving slowly towards the estab-lishment of venture capital subsidiaries not unlike the American SBICs. The Midland Bank, for example, is a shareholder in Moracrest, an investment company set up in December 1976 with industrialists on the staff, whose express purpose is to invest venture capital. It has yet to get its hands dirty with really new technology – mechanical handling, computer software and extruded plastic bottles are its most adventurous investments to date – and it's hardly in danger of breaking the bank – its authorised (but not necessarily issued) share capital is a mere £15 million, and the Midland's third of this looks insignificant beside the banks' total lending in 1976 of £7·26 *billion* – but it's a start.

With the exception of the merchant banks – whom we shall meet at the second phase of the venture capital story – that concludes the list of significant sources of risk money in Britain.

It is time now to meet two entrepreneurs who have run the gamut of the British financial institutions and emerged successful, although without any help whatsoever from the traditional sources of venture capital. They are two very different kinds of person, operating at opposite ends of England. Arthur Crump hails from Poole in Dorset, where he used to work for Plessey and GEC as an electronics design engineer before he set off on his own to establish Spectronics. He began in a humble way, establishing Spectronics on a trading estate just outside Poole to do contract research for other companies. In his first year he was joined by Dennis Lockwood and Gerald Thomas, as technical director and production manager respectively, and between the three of them they managed – against their own collateral – to raise the £7000 which was enough to keep them going until they had designed their first major innovation, a thermal printer.

The thermal printer used heat-sensitised paper on which to record the print-out from a microprocessor control, useful for storing routine results from remote monitoring units in factories, either to replace routine inspectors or to operate in unsavoury environments too hot or unhealthy for humans. Their £7000 just ran to the development of the prototype; Spectronics needed more money to manufacture and market their product so, like many a young company before them, they took the prototype to the NRDC. And to their delight they succeeded in their quest – the NRDC offered to put in £20,000.

It was not, however, nearly enough. Spectronics really needed £50,000 and, what was worse, the money came in dribs and drabs. Spectronics invoiced the NRDC in the normal way, but close monitoring of the accounts delayed the payments they so badly needed, and Spectronics ran into hopeless cash-flow problems. Nor was the money cheap – interest was fixed at 17 per cent – and the NRDC did not offer to back up its financial help with management advice. Today the situation might be different; the NRDC acknowledges that small firms do not live by money alone and it is attempting to recruit experienced industrialists to advise and help the inexperienced innovator, but back in 1973 Crump found himself sinking fast and in desperate need of cash. He found more money by what must be the most primitive of all business methods, the small ads in the *Financial Times*. As Crump put it, 'We were inundated with all sorts of enquiries, an awful lot of them were from cranks, and awful lot of others were from what I can only describe as dubious characters, but some were genuine and we did do a deal with a person whom we felt was genuine.'

Spectronics' backing, thanks to Wise Estates, rose to £60,000 and the firm were able to proceed with manufacturing the thermal printer, which never became a spectacular success but which turns over steadily and today represents the mainstay of the company's output.

Spectronics' troubles began when Wise Estates declined to follow their first investment with a second one. The reasons for their refusal are obscure: another venture capital project in which they were involved failed completely, and this must have influenced them; it is said they were frustrated by the lack of quick returns from Spectronics; their representative on the Spectronics board was having little say in the running of the company – it could have been any or all of these factors. Spectronics, having survived round one fairly successfully, were about to enter the second stage of financing in a very parlous state.

The Systime story began even more shakily than Spectronics. John Gow was working in Lancashire for the British subsidiary of Digital Equipment Corporation, itself one of the classic examples of American venture capital start-ups over the past decade. Gow was selling computer hardware to customers in the North of England and was gradually learning how few of his customers really knew precisely what tasks their computers were capable of performing and hence what hard or software they really needed to buy. It so happened that one of Digital's customers, a discount warehouse, found itself in trouble when a software house decided (after eight weeks considering the problem) that it could not write the program needed for the new computer; John Gow offered to do the job in six weeks, and with his wife and a friend he succeeded in completing the task with just four hours to spare. It earned him £2000, but what was more important was the lesson it gave him: that here was a hole in the computer market that was not being effectively filled. With Digital's full support, John Gow gave up his job, sold his car for a further £800 and set up in business on his own to design computer systems and install the necessary hardware.

The computers he was selling cost around £60,000 each, yet his total backing was just £2800; barely enough to rent the canteen of a disused mill and to hire a clutch of computer programmers. Digital were generous; they consciously permitted him to delay payment of bills until he had received his cash from the client. Things ticked over at first, partly because the staff proved willing to wait for their paychecks until such time as Systime had money in the bank. Life got more difficult when new staff actually demanded payment at the end of each month and the crisis arrived when, at the end of one month, Gow found himself £4000 in the red, a figure he only covered by raising the mortgage on his house. In 1973 Gow was probably even closer than Arthur Crump to the complete failure of his venture.

What saved Systime was one of their own customers. Musichire are a Leeds firm who hire or sell one-armed bandits and pinball machines. They had bought a computer from Digital but were running into problems and Systime were called in. John Gow succeeded in selling them, not only his system, but also a range of new hardware. The financial director of Musichire was a young accountant named John Parkinson, and he saw in Gow, not only a man in need of financial help, but also a salesman whose enterprise deserved more support than it was getting. The board of Musichire was at the time looking for ways to diversify (the son of the chairman needed a small company on which to cut his managerial teeth) and Parkinson was able to persuade the company to buy 26 per cent of Systime, to guarantee a bank overdraft of £50,000, and to put Parkinson himself on the board of Systime as financial director.

In effect, then, it was not from the venture capital institutions but from other sectors of industry that Systime got their start-up money. Digital Equipment Corporation were generous creditors, Musichire both as customer and as shareholder enabled the young company to get itself into some kind of shape and – what was most important – the arrival of John Parkinson put order into Gow's cash-flow nightmare. Parkinson himself didn't find the early days at all easy; he tells today of sending invoices out on a Monday, followed the next day by a man from Systime who was instructed not to quit the client's premises until he had a cheque in his hand.

By 1974, both companies were surviving, but neither could put their hand on their corporate heart and swear that in a year's time they would still be in business. In technologies as complex as microelectronics and computer systems, customers prefer to buy from secure sources for fear something should go wrong with the product and there will be no one around to put it right, so both firms needed not only more money in order to expand, but a reputable backer whom clients could trust not to let their investees go out of business. So both Spectronics and Systime set out for the City of London to see whether the streets there really were paved with gold.

In round two of funding most companies need between £50,000 and £1 million, and at first sight the money looks easier to come by. The merchant banks, in particular, are happy to get involved in growing concerns, and the ICFC finances many more ventures of this kind than the start-ups with which, as we've seen, it has a less than happy record. Yet both companies found round two even more difficult than the first, and the reason is once again best expressed by Gordon Richardson: 'I do sometimes wonder whether the experience of those who have entered the venture capital field might not have been happier had they developed a greater capacity to monitor and judge markets and products rather than just balance sheets and cash flows.' The Spectronics story carries this failing to its nadir. Arthur Crump tells how he was handled when he presented his thermal printer for assessment by the ICFC: 'After quite a few months of negotiation I discovered that the person doing this so-called market survey had devoted a single morning to the job, and that the previous day the person concerned had been doing research on ladies' underwear and the day after on ice cream. Now I actually rang her up and I asked how she was proposing to set about it, and she said, "Oh, we've done quite a lot of it already", so I said, "That's nice to know; how are the results going?" and she said, "Oh, there's not a lot of call for that kind of teleprinter and, um, photocopier", and I said, "It's not a teleprinter and it's not a photocopier", but I lost my money.'

John Gow expressed his reaction to the financiers a little more forcibly: 'We called them plastic men,' he said, 'because we couldn't find out what motivated them as individuals.' Where Arthur Crump simply failed to raise any offers of second-round financing from any of the 35 firms he visited, Systime were in fact offered a number of deals but refused them because they regarded the terms – or the people behind them – as unacceptable. The ICFC offered a loan, but again it was at 17 per cent fixed interest, which would have meant a millstone round Systime's neck. One leading merchant bank was on the point of concluding a deal when John Gow's dislike for 'plastic men' got in the way. John Parkinson describes how, after a series of preliminary meetings with the bankers, during which both sides had made a lot of headway, they were called down to meet one of the directors. Parkinson put a lot of effort into preparing the figures and presenting them in the manner he knew the banks liked. The director then asked them what Systime expected to be doing in two or three years time. John Gow at that point broke the suspicious silence with which he had been contemplating the banker. 'After we've got computers cracked', he said, 'I thought we'd have a go at building aeroplanes.' There was a nervous pause, and then the director turned back to Parkinson and asked him icily, 'Tell me, has your partner any experience in dealing with financial institutions?' Once Parkinson had, as he tells it, 'kicked John all the way to the station', the two men reflected over a couple of drinks on the train that they had at least retained their independence, and that their recently acquired cash-flow skills would probably see them through another year or so.

In the cold war that seems to exist between the men of money and the men of ideas, it isn't only the former who are to blame. To quote Gordon Richardson once more: 'Small businessmen

must share more of their equity than their instincts urge them to.'
To put it more explicitly, they must be prepared to accept a
greater degree of control from their backers than they seem, at
present, willing to do. We saw in the last chapter how David Lee
of Qume was happy to let the venture capitalist Paul Wythes
select both a product and a president for the new company, and
that's a far cry from the attitude of John Gow. Gow, of course,
replies that he would have been happy to accept control from
someone whose abilities he respected, but that such a person was
not to be found among Britain's financiers . . . and so the vicious
circle continues.

Systime kept afloat, despite their refusal to accept backing
from either the ICFC or the merchant banks, mainly because the
Musichire connection encouraged the local Yorkshire Bank to
raise their overdraft limit by a further £100,000, while Musichire
in turn took a £100,000 debenture – a loan with first call on
Systime's assets. The company's performance was spectacular:
from a turnover of £600,000 in 1974 it grew to over £4 million in
1977 and an estimated £6 million in 1978. It had by now moved
into the rest of the old mill building and brought in girls from the
nearby declining shirt factories and retrained them to assemble
computers. By now the two Johns were buying in very few
components from outside; they used the company's own design
skills to produce not just the computer programs, but also
complete hardware systems. John Parkinson then decided to
leave Musichire and to join Systime as chairman; he and Gow
complement each other perfectly – the salesman who can't keep
a tight enough rein on his own enterprise, the financial expert
who knows just how much freedom to permit his brilliant
colleague. They have between them enough ability and arrogance
to make Systime perhaps the most thrusting and successful young
company in Britain today.

It was the old Gow arrogance that prompted his reply to a
telephone call from the National Enterprise Board in the spring
of 1977. John Pearce of the NEB was trying to explain to Gow
that the NEB was planning to establish a group of dynamic
companies operating in the computer field, in the hope of creating
a coherent electronics industry in Britain that might start to claw
back from the Americans some of the enormous lead that Silicon
Valley and other centres of electronic excellence had secured.
John Gow didn't want to know: 'We're no ——— lame duck', he
said, and put the phone down on Pearce. A week later, Pearce
rang again and suggested that Gow should at least come to
London and talk about it. Gow said that if the NEB was that
keen, then Pearce should come up to Leeds . . . and Pearce did.
'The chemistry was right almost from the start,' says Gow. 'He

had had a lot of time in the computer software industry, knew what he was talking about and as he walked round the place he was spot on with his appraisals of almost every situation. Within an hour we had hammered out the basis of a deal.' It took only three months to conclude that deal: over the next four years Systime were to have an option on £700,000 from the NEB at a variable interest rate, with a five-year holiday before the loan needed to be repaid. The NEB paid a quarter of a million pounds for 26 per cent of Systime's equity and, in return, John Gow joined the board of Insac, the NEB's holding company of combined software and hardware companies, giving them both the benefit of his experience and, in theory, the promise of co-operation with their joint decisions.

Back at Spectronics, things had not been going nearly so well. The company had now developed their second major new product, the Printacom. This device in effect turned any telephone into a telex machine. It consisted of a portable keyboard with a memory into which the typed message could be entered. The text could then be sent down the telephone line to another Printacom, simply by joining both sets to acoustic couplers and pressing a 'transmit' button. It was a simple and ingenious product, with applications both in countries with inadequate telex facilities, and in the most advanced countries, where roving salesmen or journalists cannot guarantee to be near a telex machine, but can find a telephone. The problem was that Spectronics were far from having the money to develop their new product; on the contrary, they were sinking further and further into debt.

Arthur Crump says that the summer of 1977 brought him close to a breakdown: he shut himself away at home with a pile of science fiction books, terrified to answer the telephone in case it carried a demand he could not meet. What finally arrived, though, was an offer he couldn't refuse. Anwar Farid, an Abu Dhabi businessman, was so frustrated by the appalling telex facilities in the Middle East that news of the Printacom brought him, cheque book in hand, to London. He offered £250,000 down, another £500,000 later, and then any more backing that might be needed. The consultant who spent just one day introducing Farid to Spectronics collected £2000 for his efforts and then moved on to another East-West liaison. For Crump, the result brought mixed emotions: he was delighted to become an employee again (self-employment had brought little but agony for him) and a 10-year contract with what he described as a 'handsome' salary enabled him to go to work happy and surge ahead with the knowledge that his backer would pay the cheques. His sadness on signing came from the fact that the profits he expects Spectronics to earn will go, not into British pockets, but into Middle-Eastern coffers.

Since the signing, Crump's sadness has grown. Farid, after a few months, decided to replace Crump as chief executive and to relegate him to marketing director. In essence, he was behaving just like the American venture capitalists we met in the last chapter, but Crump feels humiliated by the demotion. His wife, Anne, has left her post as company secretary (both their jobs have been filled by Arabs) and is now retained as freelance public relations consultant.

The number of morals that could be drawn from the two stories of Systime and Spectronics is a large one. The natural response to accusations of the kind I have outlined is to find someone or something else – usually 'the system' – to blame. It is certainly true that there is very little incentive to risk investment in new technologies in a financial climate where even the rare success story is, first, going to be much less profitable than its American equivalent (our government just absorbs too much of the turnover) and, second, where the profit, when it does arrive, is taxed at a much higher rate than in America (while losses cannot be deducted from taxation). To improve this situation it would be good to see Britain introduce a healthy margin between capital gains earned from new technology ventures, on the one hand, and personal taxation on the other, and also to see related losses counted as deductibles. But more important than fiscal measures is the need to create a climate in which the entrepreneur is encouraged both by the Government and by the finance houses, instead of feeling harried by people he does not like or respect. We asked John Parkinson what he would do differently now that he reckons he knows how the City functions, and his reply is worth quoting in full: 'The first thing I would do differently is to aim this time to go straight to the top; we wasted an awful lot of time with people who couldn't take decisions. The second point is that, because nobody really did a very fantastic technological survey of us, I think it would have been possible to pad the figures; it would have been possible actually to come to a deal that some of the institutions probably would have gone for. What we would have done was say, "Yes, we'll repay the loan over X period of time", knowing damn well that we couldn't, and the upshot of it would have been that if we'd have angled the figures right, the investor wouldn't have been able to pull out.' That's a terrifying indictment of Britain's financiers, if it's true.

A final note, however, is that the financiers are not solely to blame. It is right that the banks should take some of the opprobrium, since theirs is the principal responsibility in this field; they exist to lend money at a profit and to create wealth for the nation. But there is around £30 billion in Britain tied up in pension funds, in insurance companies and in building societies – and virtually none of this money (half the private savings in Britain!) finds its way into venture capital. In America, though I hate to say it again, the situation is different. Many of the venture capital outfits (including Reid Dennis's IVA) are backed by money from these sources, and they often invest directly. Our fund managers should, somehow, be forced to account for their failure to enter this field. And what of British industrial wealth? The sad fact here is that most of Britain's most enterprising companies, such as GEC, Lucas, Ferranti and others, have actually taken their shopping baskets to Silicon Valley to buy new companies out there, and more than one American risk business owes its recent survival to British venture capital. It's a depressing note on which to end a book dedicated, in all other respects, to British initiatives in the fields of design and industry.

Where Are They Now?

Throughout the preceding chapters I have hinted that the stories we featured in 'The Risk Business' unfolded further between the time the programmes were transmitted and the time of writing this book. Ron Ellis of Leyland Truck and Bus had been replaced by Desmond Pitcher, who has himself subsequently been removed. The ICI Merolite saga had, as anticipated, ended in disaster. Bond Worth, the weaving group, had called in the receiver, and so on.

That process has by no means finished. This postscript is written just six months after the other chapters, and yet there are few episodes that have not continued to unfold. Qume, the Californian venture-capital-based company that had made such a success of the daisy wheel printer, has now been bought out by the giant ITT company, leaving its founders and Bob Schroeder, the new President, 'multi-millionaires' – at least, that is how *Fortune* magazine describes them. In fact, ITT valued Qume at no less than $153 million. The Leyland T45 truck failed to make the October Motor Show at Birmingham in 1978, and this book's publication had actually to be delayed to coincide (it is hoped) with the truck's launch in October 1979, because of the classified information it contains. Des Pitcher has embarked on a bitter war of words with his old employers . . . but that's another story. His successor at Truck and Bus was announced in December 1978 as David Abell, a 35-year-old BL high flyer previously in charge of Special Projects who is now faced with restoring the division's profitability. Lionel Blackman has now left Pilkington, but this seems to be simply the sort of move that often lifts a man more rapidly than internal promotion. The Denovo tyre is still in production, but 1978 was one of the worst years ever for the tyre industry. America is reeling from the effects of the introduction of the steel-belted radial, which has dented the replacement market; Britain's share – even of our own market – continued to decline. Dunlop are still optimistic and have introduced another new design – the Denloc. The fact remains, however, that this is a more conventional tyre with no internal lubricant, although it is in one respect a competitor to the Denovo in that it stays on the rim in the event of a blow-out.

And so it goes on. Clarks missed their September deadline for getting the Sidebinder shoe into full production and into the shops. That in turn meant that the salesmen, who make a regular round of the retailers in October to collect repeat orders for the winter, were unable to offer this, the most important innovation Clarks had attempted that year. Perhaps chastened by their attempt to introduce polyurethane technology in the formal shoe field, Clarks' men's division had by now taken a further dramatic decision: their next range of men's 'shiny' or 'smart' shoes was to be designed and manufactured, not in Street by their own personnel, but in Northampton by an outside, contract manufacturer. What is more, Pentagram scored a notable success in relation to the new range of shoes: John McConnell suggested that they should be given the name of no less a figure than James Clark himself. The whole sales pitch was to be geared to the founder's own signature, which would be displayed prominently beneath what purported to be his commendation of the new product. Nobody is saying precisely what the reaction was back in Street to this development, either in the men's division's own factory, still struggling with the difficult manufacture of the Sidebinder, or within the Clark family itself. Lance Clark admitted to no worries at all: 'If it takes 150 years to get your name on a product, I can't imagine what they'll be producing under my name!' he jokes, but there are rumours that the Clarks of Street are not too pleased to see the hallowed name used in conjunction with a product designed and made in Northampton.

But the biggest turnaround of them all has happened in Blackburn. Edgar Pickering was, when we left him, having trouble convincing the rest of the world that the Multicolour machine would ever be capable of sustained and reliable carpet manufacture. To prove his case, he instructed his plant to run the machine for 24 hours a day over a period of two or three weeks in order, as he says, 'to prove once and for all to the sceptics that the machine was no pipe dream, but a viable piece of carpet-producing machinery suitable for future patterned carpet production. The carpet that was made during this period was beautiful, with a first-class design, good colours and excellent quality.' But – and irony can seldom have been so bitter – the prearranged client for the order was, of all people, Rivington Carpets, part of the ill-fated Bond Worth group. A week or so after the huge consignment was delivered, Bond Worth called in the receiver and Pickering lost any chance of being paid for the carpet. It cost the fledgling division about £150,000. Pickering's colleagues in London – he was by now part of the mighty Sears Holdings group – decided that this misfortune was the direct result of Edgar's unwise decision to dabble in the production of carpets instead of sticking to what he understood best, making the machines, and leaving it to the carpet manufacturers to produce the final product.

Reluctantly, Edgar agreed that the Multicolour division should be sold off to Bowater Carpets. It was extremely bitter for him to witness another company reaping the harvest of his own risk-taking: 'You know as well as I do that when you pioneer a new type of machine it is never a bed of roses . . . I had no intention of carrying on with people who had such limited vision.'

Edgar Pickering and Sears Holdings came to what he describes as 'a reasonably amicable understanding' which allowed him to leave at the end of June 1978. Now comes the ultimate irony: Edgar has joined up with his old rivals, the Americans. He is now handling the European affairs of the Tuftco group, working under the company name of Pickering Enterprises. The firm he founded and built from nothing still trades under the title of Edgar Pickering Limited.

Now, it is true that the vast majority of those who work in industry in Britain do in fact work in unattractive surroundings, and that their jobs are uneventful and unrewarding. And this is true, in general, of those in management as well as those on the factory floor. But I hope that by now the reader will have been convinced that there are certain pockets of activity and enterprise where the twists and turns both of fortune and of carefully planned strategems happen so swiftly that the writers or broadcasters of supposedly over-dramatic fiction would find themselves outmanoeuvred. The heartening thing is that these flurries of activity occur just where they should take place, as the direct result of individual entrepreneurs like Edgar Pickering and the others about whom I have written. I made the claim in the introduction to this book that all those about whom I have written deserved – and carried with honour – the title of 'designer', and I hope also that the reader will have been made aware of just how varied are the activities of designers in today's industrial scene – and of just how great is the responsibility they carry in many cases. I would finish with an apology, because I am well aware that I have stretched the title 'designer' far more broadly than is usual (I said in the introduction that some of our dramatis personae – including Edgar – would be surprised to hear themselves described as designers at all). But I should like, instead, to end with a challenge.

If it is not customary to think of managers of truck divisions, of scientists and inventors, of entrepreneurs and the rest as 'designers', nor for designers to imagine that they will need as broad a range of training and experience as these men undoubtedly require, then isn't it about time that the art colleges and other design hot-houses changed their attitudes and gave them this training? And isn't it also time that industrialists themselves broadened their view to count 'design', not as a totally separate and somewhat recondite art, but as a natural part of their own portfolio of skills – and above all as one of the few remaining advantages that we can still claim over the rapidly developing nations that are threatening our industrial survival?

Zuleika Dobson uttered the provocative remark, 'I don't know anything about music really, but I know what I like.' Alas, too many chief executives in British industry would happily say the same about the design of their companies' products. What binds the characters in this book together is the fact that they all know a great deal about the design of their various products; in many cases it has been their principal preoccupation. What also binds them together is that they have, without exception, taken a gamble on their own entrepreneurial skills and that, in more cases than not, this gamble paid off. So long as people like this continue to enter our manufacturing businesses, and so long as industry is aware that it must nurture and encourage them, I believe that Britain will continue not only to survive but to prosper. Prosperity, if you like, by Design.